End

Every once in awhile I ho .... with a patient who is able to teach me a magnitude of lessons both by example and by sharing his experience, Tom Holtackers is one such patient.

When you first meet Tom, you learn quickly that he has an indomitable spirit, but you might assume that has always been the case and he has approached coping with MS with a "can do" spirit. Tom tells us in his story that disability is truly a state of mind, but with the impact of his story comes the fact that this is a discovery he made after many years of facing the challenges of MS. He suffered, he was uncertain, he persevered, but eventually he conquered.

There are many words to describe Tom's persistence in the face of adversity, and many to describe his willingness to share his story openly and honestly. None seems to adequately express the gift Tom has given in the way he has lived his life and willingness to share his story.

Around the campus where we both work, Tom has been inspirational to many of us who have faced challenges of our own. If Tom didn't give up, we wouldn't give up either. I hope you find in Tom's story the courage to redefine your life by abilities not by the limits created by illness or injury.

Robin G. Molella, MD, MPH

Readers will appreciate this sincere, honest and insightful account of a life lived with multiple sclerosis. Tom provides a compelling narrative of the developing toll that multiple sclerosis took on not only his physical function, but more importantly his self concept and relationships. The most instructive aspect of the book is his ongoing translation of the disease into an opportunity to be of service to others. He ultimately redefines multiple sclerosis as a gift, a gift that required him to change his self-perception and self-definition. I recommend this book to individuals struggling with not just multiple sclerosis, but also any chronic illness that requires ongoing adaptation to change. *Daniel E. Rohe Ph.D. Past President, Division of Rehabilitation Psychology, American Psychological Association*

Tom's story is both captivating and compelling. He shares his journey with a genuine and sincere style that brings you inside a life with a chronic, incurable disease. Tom's optimism and problem-solving style, along with his conviction that people with MS must be empowered to identify solutions and work for those solutions themselves, brings hope to all aspects of his life. His story is well worth reading. *Maureen Reeder, President National MS Society, Minnesota Chapter*

This is a remarkable piece of work. Tom is an extraordinarily talented writer and a courageous man to share his story with the rest of us. This is extremely powerful. There is much in this book for all of us. *John Noseworthy, MD*

As a person with MS for over 30 years, I acknowledge Tom's willingness to be vulnerable from the outside in and the inside out of his life since his diagnosis of MS. Throughout the book he is authentic, honest, gritty, sometimes sad and depressed, profound, intense, loving, powerful, angry, tender, tough, strong, wise and filled with great passion for life and wholeness. These describe who he is and what makes the book so meaningful and powerful.

Louann S. Replogle

Tom's heartfelt honesty makes **It Takes Courage** a must read. His boldness from darkness into light raises us to a new level of healing showing us how to embrace our future, no matter what. *Jackie Waldman, author, The Courage to Give series*

It Takes Courage

Coping With Chronic Illness

Thomas R. Holtackers, PT

Published by Courage Press
MSSUX Unlimited
P.O. Box 7257
Rochester, Minnesota 55903-7257

ISBN 978-0-9789333-0-2

Library of Congress Control Number: 2006910539

For more information:
visit the website
www.msspokenhere.com
or e-mail
ittakescourage@msspokenhere.com.

About the author: Thomas Holtackers is a graduate of Montclair State College and the Mayo Clinic Program in Physical Therapy. He recently retired from the Mayo Clinic after 33 years and resides in Rochester, MN where he enjoys writing and speaking about his experiences coping with multiple sclerosis. He serves on various state and national committees for the National Multiple Sclerosis Society and is an avid fundraiser for MS research. He has received numerous awards for his active involvement with the MS Society and physical therapy organizations. Most notably, he was inducted into the National MS Society's Volunteer Hall of Fame; received the Minnesota Physical Therapy Association's Outstanding Service Award; as well as awarded Outstanding Alumnus Awards from the Mayo Clinic Physical Therapy Program and Montclair State College.

"The cover photograph was taken just as I crossed the finish line of a 10-mile race in 1984. Though totally exhausted and only able to raise my arms to shoulder height, I was able to express my elation at having finished four seconds in front of the first place runner! Winning the race and the "Courage" t-shirt became the inspiration for the title of this book."

-- *Thomas Holtackers*

Dedication

It Takes Courage is devoted to all who live with the day-to-day struggles of living with chronic illness, their life partners and healthcare providers, and to the researchers who will someday end the devastating effects of all chronic diseases.

Most of all it is dedicated to my friends, fellow support group members, volunteers, donors, clients and patients with multiple sclerosis, as well as their care partners who have provided me with the opportunity to learn from their trials with the disease. More specifically it is dedicated to my friends who have passed before me because of MS - Constance, Earl and Ginny – from whom I have learned so much to help me cope with _my_ MS.

<u>Acknowledgements</u>

A profound thank you to my children, Greta and Grant; their mother, Muriel; and my brother Dave for their undying love and continued support.

Thank you to all the staff and committee members of the National MS Society, Minnesota Chapter and staff of the National MS Society for their acknowledgement of my volunteer commitments from which I have learned so much about MS and myself.

A roaring thank you to my editor, Cindy Cantu, for her valuable constructive criticism.

Thank you to the Mayo Clinic medical and surgical physicians; physical and occupational therapists; nurses; and patient education staff for their expertise.

And finally, a hearty thanks to the owners of the Dunn Bros. in Rochester, MN, Dennis and Lyn, and their fabulous staff for gallons of delicious coffee, their gentle nudges to continue with my quest and for providing a nurturing "home away from home."

Foreword

Nearly 25 years ago as a young neurologist in training, I decided to pursue a career in clinical research focusing on the human demyelinating diseases, particularly multiple sclerosis (MS). My reason for doing this was simple. I had found myself moved and inspired by the personal courage demonstrated on a daily basis by the victims of these diseases. Many of them, like me at that time, were young people with their entire lives ahead of them. For many, the promise of family and career had suddenly been jeopardized by the uncertainty of a poorly understood and unpredictable, serious neurological illness. There was reason for great hope as then, like now, tremendous breakthroughs in neuroscience research offered the possibility of improved treatments and, ultimately, possibly even prevention or cure for this disease

The time has gone quickly these last two decades. Countless times I have been told by patients, "Remember-keep at it and take no coffee breaks as we need better treatments or, preferably a cure now!" We have seen many advances in MS research, particularly in early diagnosis and in the development of partially effective therapies that reduce relapse frequency and severity. In the related condition neuromyelitis optica ("Devic's disease"), we now have a useful diagnostic blood test of this and, I believe soon, we will understand more about the specific mechanisms of injury in this form of demyelinating disease. These findings should soon be followed by increasingly effective therapies for neuromyelitis optica. Additionally, positive strides are being made to identify more effective therapies for MS, but there is much more that needs to be done.

In this remarkable book, Tom has pulled back the curtain and shown us the reality of dealing with chronic illness. He has courageously shared personal moments with us and demonstrated how he and his loved ones have struggled day by day to remain positive and to keep the upper hand on this nasty illness. Tom has chosen to forgo pride and share this struggle with his readers. As such, he has provided a remarkable example for each of us.

The lessons revealed in this personal account go beyond those that might seem to apply only to patients with neurological disease in general, or MS, specifically. Each of us at some time in our lives are or will be patients and each of us, whether currently healthy or not, would do well to read Tom's words and reflect on their meaning to us.

Many years ago, a patient of mine with long-standing MS gave me some advice. "Tell your patients to let MS be a nuisance but never to let it become a monster." I have shared this wisdom with many patients and, I suspect, some of found it helpful. Tom continues to live this life lesson courageously and with grace.

I am deeply honored that he has given me an opportunity to read an advanced draft of this remarkable book. I know it will touch the lives of many.

John Noseworthy, M.D.
Rochester, MN

Table of Contents

Introduction

"It Takes Courage" is about coping with the adversities of living with a chronic illness and is a testimony of my journey with destiny. Multiple sclerosis (MS) is my fate and the burden I must bear - it is the weakness that strengthens my character. It is a part of me, but it is not who I am. It has sculpted my uniqueness, but I am the one who defines who I am!

MS is an illness that has the potential to affect all of my physical, emotional and mental domains. It is a chronic, progressive disease of the central nervous system that can affect any function of my body controlled by the brain and spinal cord. It comes in different degrees, from the mild to the harsh, and with limitations from subtle to severe. Fortunately, most of us with MS live normal lives. We get married, raise families, have jobs, retire and die. We worry about our kids and parents, experience the agonies and pleasures of life, and engage in the future with hope and uncertainty. But, the essence of the disease and accompanying disability adds to the difficulties during life's voyage and, for most, has major life-altering consequences.

As peculiar as it may sound, I am fortunate in having MS. Yes, MS has taken me through periods of despair and disappointment, and has weakened and deformed my body, but my struggle to cope with its effects has strengthened my spirit and resolve. My struggle has provided me with triumph and incentive. My goal in writing this book is to share my journey - my mistakes and successes, realizations and revelations, losses and rewards. Embedded in these episodes are unique transitions. In the beginning, my story is that of a victim; it is the validation of suffering where I grieved my losses, denied my deterioration and feared the future. Later, I make a transition from being a victim to a survivor by being able to tolerate my losses and confront the future **_in spite of_** the adversity I may have to endure. Finally, I break loose from my story's meaningless bondage as I put my past in the past and embrace the present by creating a future full of possibilities and inspiration **_because of_** my illness!

A disease over which I have no control broadsided me. It brought disability into my life. Granted, my body is predestined to decline with age, to fail through nature's planned obsolescence; that's life. But, a part of my body's deterioration could occur through risky lifestyle behaviors or benign neglect over which I do have control. It takes courage for me to minimize my disability due to disease and aging, manage those factors over which I do have control and maximize my life's potential. While life, in general, requires continual adjustment no matter what the course, coping with the adversity of a chronic illness in positive ways has influenced me in a way to generate more courage to reach deep within to maintain quality and equilibrium.

This narrative is for all who struggle with the adversity of a chronic illness. While there is struggle no matter what the malady is, it is the healthy reaction to that adversity that builds and strengthens character to endure the journey!

Here is my journey.

Chapter One

My Story Begins... From Victim to Survivor

It took courage to tell my
story over and over
even though others didn't want
to hear it.
It took not heroic courage,
but a quiet, common courage -
something we all possess.

My first encounter

The onset was subtle and insidious; no big events, no eruptions, just a slow erosion of my physical function. I didn't foresee the gradual wear and tear of my abilities; I was becoming a victim of a cold, cruel, glacier-like behemoth called multiple sclerosis (MS) and I didn't know it.

In retrospect, my first symptom of multiple sclerosis occurred in 1968 - 12 years prior to my diagnosis! I was in the midst of early adulthood when my marriage and teaching career were in their infancy. I was teaching physical education and coaching football at a high school in New Jersey. I had been happily married little over a year; my wife was also a physical education teacher. I was healthy, strong and energetic, and at the peak of my physical prowess. I felt on top of the world!

It was after a very intense football game when I encountered my first symptom of MS. Initially, I thought the spot in my right eye's vision was one of those dust floaters that follows the movement of the eye, but this one was very large and very noticeable. The spot had become larger over several days before I decided to seek medical attention. The eye doctor told me that I had optic neuritis, an inflammation of the eye's nerve. He said it was common for people who were under a lot of stress to develop this condition. He cited several references to soldiers in combat who developed this problem before, during and after battle. He said it would go away in approximately 2-3 weeks and not to worry - it did and I didn't. I went on with my wondrous life without regard to any possible problem with my nervous system. I had no reoccurrence of optic neuritis ever again.

In 1970, I left teaching to pursue a career in physical therapy without knowing I had the beginnings of MS. My wife and I pulled up our New Jersey stakes and moved to Rochester, Minnesota where I spent two years getting my degree at the Mayo Clinic during which my wife taught in the Rochester school system. Right after graduation I began working at Mayo as a physical therapist in the Respiratory Care Intensive Care Unit. My job was to help rehabilitate severely ill patients; it was a very challenging and rewarding job. I became very skilled at weaning patients with respiratory failure from mechanical ventilation. It was physically taxing, but I had no difficulty in fulfilling my responsibilities; I was strong and energetic. My wife and I were starting a new life with all the anticipation of a future filled with pursuing our careers and plans of having a family together. Little did we know the trials and tribulations of life would interfere with those plans.

Fatigue creeps into my life

It was approximately one year after starting my new physical therapy career when I began experiencing occasional bouts of extreme exhaustion for no apparent reason. This fatigue was so overwhelming at times, I could hardly function. I would have to stop what I was doing and rest. It would hit very quickly and without warning. It wasn't a sleepy-tired type of fatigue; it was more like someone pulled the plug on my storage of energy and I was drained. It was like having the flu so bad I couldn't get out of bed, but I didn't have the flu and other than being fatigued, I felt fine!

I was working full-time, which was physically, mentally and emotionally stressful plus I was remodeling an old house, which was also very taxing. It was these things and more that I reasoned were the causes of my fatigue. These bouts wouldn't last long and seemed to be more predominate when I was working on the house. It didn't affect my work at the hospital.

More difficulties develop

I also noticed other problems while I was trying out for the therapist's softball team in the spring of 1973. Although it wasn't my favorite sport, I loved competition and exercise so I thought I would give it a try. I had always thought of myself as well coordinated enough to participate in just about any sport. This was one of the reasons I became a physical education teacher and coach. During my tryout for the team, I had difficulty running after and catching fly balls. My feet and legs felt clumsy and cumbersome, definitely out of my norm. It seemed as if the harder I tried the more of a klutz I became. I gracefully bowed out of the softball team, subconsciously blaming my awkwardness on my being out of shape.

Later that summer, my wife and I went on vacation, back to New Jersey where we grew up. We were visiting her family at a lake where, ironically, we both learned how to swim - she at the beach and me at the dam on the other side of the lake, but that's another story. It was a warm, sunny June afternoon on the beach and we were there to soak up some rays, relax, and catch up on the local chitchat. I'm not sure which became hotter, the sun or the gossip, but after awhile of absorbing too much of both, I began to feel uneasy. I was no stranger to the sun, being a former lifeguard and used to working outdoors. I knew what too much sun could do but this was different. I was well hydrated; I didn't feel sick but I felt very heavy and weak. I felt as if my breathing was labored, like I needed to take a deep breath, but when I tried, I couldn't do it real well. I felt floppy and flimsy and became fearful of what was happening. I knew I had to do something to get out of the sun and cool off. The lake water looked so inviting. I thought, "Oh, if I could only get into the water, I'd be better!" I tried to stand, only to fall back down onto the blanket on which we were sitting. I noticed subtle glances from those around me, which caused me to pause. After a few minutes I tried again, only to fall down again, but this time with more force. Now I was really feeling uncomfortable, not only physically, but emotionally. I was scared and felt as if the whole beach was watching me. I knew I had to get into the water and fast. Despite what anyone might think, I started to crawl across the short distance from the blanket to the water. Thank goodness, we weren't sitting in the middle of the beach; I don't think I would have made it. I must have looked comical, a grown man crawling on the beach, but at that point, I didn't care. All I knew was that I had to cool off or succumb

As I entered the water and felt the coolness of the lake water envelope my body, I experienced an immediate release of bondage from that weak, heavy feeling. It was cathartic, almost orgasmic, like a sensual rush of relief. As I slipped my head beneath the water, I imagined a puff of vapor rising from the surface of the lake, like the steam produced from the blacksmith's red-hot horseshoe as he plunges it into a bucket of water. What a relief! What a contrast between the frailties I felt on the hot beach and the energy I was now feeling in the refreshing, cool water. I felt strong and energetic again.

I swam around for a while, trying to act as if nothing had ever happened. But, then it struck me; I will eventually have to get out of the water and face the people on the beach. I didn't want to get out, for I couldn't forget the incident on the blanket, not just the weakness I displayed, but also the stares from the faces of those around me. It was most unforgettable, my perception of the perceptions of those around me. What were they thinking? They must have been confused. One moment I'm strong and vivacious and the next, I'm falling down and crawling on the beach. And then next, I'm swimming around the lake as if nothing happened. I was supposed to be the strong one; the athlete, the physical education teacher, the coach and now the physical therapist. I exhibited frailty, feebleness and vulnerability. I was embarrassed; I felt ashamed and disgraced, but I also felt alone, extremely alone.

Our vacation at the lake went on without another incident. Afterward, we returned home to the grind of our jobs, remodeling our old farmhouse and to a new dimension, planning to have a family.

I didn't connect the incident on the beach with the clumsiness during the softball tryouts or the sudden episodes of fatigue I had experienced previously. However, later that fall when I began playing volleyball for our local YMCA I was reminded of it. This wasn't recreational, Wednesday-night-down-at-the-grade-school-gym type of volleyball. This was a highly competitive, United States Volleyball

Association-sanctioned YMCA league for which our team trained hard. The team was comprised of teachers, computer programmers, doctors and other professionals. During the fall and winter, we would travel to other Y's in our area to play their teams. I wasn't a starting player on the team, but for my 5'11" frame I could normally jump high enough to grab the rim of a 10-foot basketball hoop and had no trouble spiking a volleyball over the 8-foot volleyball net.

It was just before the beginning of my third year on the team that I started to train for the upcoming season. When we had our first practice, I quickly realized there was something wrong. I could barely touch the net of the basketball hoop and my volleyball spikes were barely clearing the net. My side-to-side movement to retrieve opponent's spikes was also limited. I could barely keep up with the drills and at the end of practice sessions I was totally drained of energy, similar to the feelings I had with the whole "summer at the beach" incident, which I had chalked up as a fluke. I continued to go to the practices, but they were becoming very frustrating for I wasn't getting any better. I couldn't jump as high or move as fast as I did the year before. I figured I was just about to turn

30 years old and mused, "If this is what being 30 is all about, I wonder what turning 40 and 50 will be like?" Again, like with the softball team, I reasoned that in addition to getting older, I was very busy at a new job and remodeling an old farmhouse, plus planning to raise a family, etc. It was those factors, I told myself, which explained the differences in my condition from the year before. And, I suppose, for those reasons and more, I justified that I hadn't trained throughout the year as I had during other years. I hadn't stayed in shape and I was feeling the impact.

I was looking forward to the competition of the upcoming season and I intended to train energetically, thinking I could train out of this fatigue through hard work as I had done many times previously. However, the tougher I trained, the worse my fatigue became. In the past, fatigue was a motivator to accept the challenge to train harder. With these efforts, there had been reward - increased strength, more endurance and better performance. I wasn't familiar with this new type of fatigue. It felt different than before. It was demoralizing rather than motivating. There were no rewards to compliment my efforts, only failure and frustration. But, in absolute denial of thinking there was anything wrong with my body, I continued to train that much harder, only to become even more fatigued.

My ability to complete my daily tasks was beginning to be compromised by my fatigue and my attempts to overpower it. I needed my energy for work and to prepare our home for the anticipated arrival of our first child. The resolution of my conflict between expending energy with these necessities as opposed to that of training for volleyball took little brainpower. I quit training and volleyball to concentrate my resources on my work and home.

Our daughter, Greta, was born in June of 1974 and later our son, Grant, was born in February 1976. My wife took time off from teaching to be with the children, so raising a family and maintaining our financial stability dominated my energy consumption.

Symptoms evolve

I was experiencing more fatigue and clumsiness during the next two years after Greta's birth and began to have periodic losses of balance. Once in awhile I would stub my toe and stumble while I was walking, just catching myself before falling. The events seemed to be aggravated by increased bouts of low energy. The more fatigued I became, the more I fumbled, stumbled and staggered. There were also times when I would get dizzy and off-balance. It might occur when I was sitting, standing or walking, the latter of which aggravated my unsteady gait. I began to realize an association with these new problems with the spontaneous onset of fatigue, the clumsiness during the softball tryouts, the collapse at the lake with the summer heat and the poor training response with the volleyball team. The link between the various symptoms was becoming more apparent.

In addition, there were also times when my hands and feet would become numb and tingling, causing me to drop things when I wasn't concentrating on holding them. Although strange sensations were seemingly unnoticeable to others, it began to affect my life. I had problems differentiating items in my pants pocket, such as coins and keys. I eventually lost the ability to feel a pulse in the wrist or neck of my patients, which was an essential part of my job.

All of these symptoms would wax and wane without predictability, which was the most frustrating part of my ordeal. I tried to relate something I did or didn't do to the onset of each symptom, but there was no such connection. For the most part, I was "normal" and free from any encumbrances, but on any given day they would arise and become noticeable to me and then disappear. While they were more of a nuisance than a threat, they were slowly becoming more and more troublesome, annoying and occasionally visible. My unsteadiness was also becoming a safety issue; for occasionally, I wouldn't catch myself in time and would crash to the floor. This became a greater concern when I was climbing a ladder or operating power tools around the house. Fortunately, I was never seriously hurt, but the bumps and bruises on my body were taking their toll. I was also becoming extremely aware of the potential to lose my balance while walking with patients and would make a conscious effort to protect their safety.

Once in a while, I would have a very sudden, strong urge to go to the bathroom, but lose the urge once I got there. I was only able to void a small amount of urine, which added to the frustration. Minutes later, the urge would return and I would run to the bathroom, only to dribble just a little once again. On occasion, I would have the urge and not make it to the bathroom in time! Being soaked with a gush of urine sent me into a panic! How embarrassing for a grown man to wet his pants. I was emotionally devastated! The only recourse for me was to go home and clean myself up. Thank God these events didn't occur very often. Fortunately, when I did go home my wife wasn't there, so I was able to hide my secret from those around me. As this began to happen more frequently, I was on constant alert for the urge and the possible accident. I worried about being incontinent at home, at work, in the car and in social situations. I made sure I had an extra pair of underpants available to me and I began to wear absorbent pads. The fear of wetting my pants not only made it difficult to focus on the tasks at hand, it was quickly eroding my self-confidence and consuming my physical energy.

I also began to experience stiffness in my legs, especially after being inactive. The stiffness would subside once I was up and moving about, but it affected my balance and fed into my staggering gait. It became more pronounced when I had the urge to urinate. It seemed as if the greater the urge to go to the bathroom, the stiffer my legs became. What a sight I must have been; staggering and stumbling in a fervent attempt to get to a bathroom to avoid incontinence.

I found myself becoming more aware of how I walked. I noticed that I would have more difficulty when I didn't concentrate on each step I took. During those situations when I lost concentration, such as when talking with someone, I would stagger and stumble more often. I likened this ataxia to a drunkard tottering after a binge. Ironically, I could literally stagger into a bar and walk out straighter after one or two beers! I also noticed I had more difficulty when I was walking with many other people around, like in a mall. I came to realize that I needed a stable, visual reference to help me walk better, such as walking as close to a wall as possible. If I walked out in the open with people going in all different directions on all sides of me, I would be more ataxic. I found myself tapping the wall with my knuckles to give me more stability. I knew I needed to use a cane for stability, but I fought it as long as possible. Eventually, however, I started using a cane and it gave me the added physical support I needed, but the emotional aspects were a mixed bag. On one hand, it helped to neutralize the perception of my stagger as being drunk, but on the other, the cane represented a progression of my condition.

Occasionally, my legs would jump for no apparent reason and, of course, occurring at untimely occasions, such as when I was driving my car or sitting in a meeting. This was annoying, yet not limiting. However, later on this jumpiness began to bother me at night when I was trying to go to sleep.

As the stiffness and jumpiness of my legs seemed to be apparent to those around me, no one ever said anything or asked if I was having problems. Even so, I was becoming more self-conscious of my physical oddities. However, it was overshadowed by the rigors of my job, raising a family and the continued remodeling of our house.

My level of fatigue and the exaggeration of other symptoms had escalated over the seven years since I first noticed any problems. I had become increasingly anxious about the possibility of one or more of these symptoms flaring up when I least needed them, such as when I was teaching a class, driving to a meeting or flying in an airplane. These neurological forces were overwhelming and devastating to my life. It was as if an energy-sucking leech was slowly consuming me. Within my relatively strong, graceful, athletic body, MS was progressively converting me into a seemingly weak, inept, cadaver-like shell.

Emotional turmoil begins taking its toll

The punishment that MS was dealing out to my physical prowess during these trying times paled in comparison to the toll it was taking on my spirit. Because the symptoms were often vague and fleeting from day to day, it caused me to wonder if it was all in my head. I thought I was imagining the symptoms that were gradually invading my body. Emotionally, MS was slowly degrading my self-esteem, diminishing my self-worth and demeaning my spirit. During those days of emotional degradation, I didn't think very well of myself; I didn't like who I thought I was going to become. I was grieving my loss of function, denying what was happening at the moment and fearing what the future was going to bring.

All of these physical and emotional problems were causing turmoil in my marriage. I wasn't a great verbal communicator with those around me to begin with, so to try to convey my frustrations with my wife was difficult. My wife was aware of my physical problems, at least the visual ones, for obviously she spent more time

17

with me than any one individual. We discussed the problems but very superficially, even after having accidents in bed during the night. Along with my predisposed lack of communication skills, having occasional bouts of impotence didn't help. Granted, this happens occasionally to many men, but with me it occurred more often than not. I tried to minimize my problems for fear of rejection, which ironically led to divorce further down my path of diminishing returns.

Seeking the cause

I sought answers for my physical problems, but found none. My primary care physician at the Mayo Clinic, with whom I had confided in from the onset, supported me through those trying years. He encouraged me to live my life as it was and to try not to focus on the changes in my body. A gallant effort, but I couldn't discount the fact that my bodily functions were declining and I had no control over the process. He referred me to specialists in Neurology and Urology, but they could only tell me there was nothing medically wrong with me; they couldn't find anything to explain these symptoms. There were no tests that said I had this condition or that illness. I was becoming more and more frustrated with being told over and over that there was nothing wrong with my body. How ironic! I was having physical problems, I worked at the most prestigious medical diagnostic institution in the world and yet no one could tell me what was wrong with me! I found myself specialist-hopping, going from one to another trying to find the cause of my predicament. This only frustrated me further because they too had no answers. I don't blame the physicians at the Mayo Clinic for not giving me answers for the cause of my symptoms. MS is very hard to diagnose, especially for someone with mild symptoms such as mine. There is no definitive test, such as a blood test, to diagnose MS. I had a spinal tap done, which involves placing a needle through the lower spine into the spinal canal to draw out spinal fluid to determine any infection in the central nervous system. It was negative. There were no scans, such as a Magnetic Resonant Imaging (MRI) that is now used to confirm the diagnosis. As a result, my diagnosis would be based on symptom history and mine was too vague to pinpoint. My only saving grace was my primary care physician who never gave up the quest to find the answers to my dilemma.

I tried to figure it out on my own. I searched through every medical textbook and journal I could get my hands on. I was looking for an answer, but fearing the worst. I wanted to know what was causing these bizarre symptoms, while simultaneously trying to deny there was anything wrong. My self-diagnosis eventually boiled down to either a brain tumor or multiple sclerosis, neither of which sounded very good.

Living with symptoms of an unknown cause and gradually becoming weaker, stiffer, slower and more fatigued caused me to become angrier and more frustrated because it seemed no one believed these things were happening to me. This lack of confirmation of my symptoms made me even more insecure. I became more withdrawn and isolated for fear of what people would see and think. I didn't want people to know I was having problems, yet paradoxically, I needed affirmation that I was having difficulties. The physical problems were annoying and sometimes caused me to stop what I was trying to do, however, the emotional trauma of not knowing what was wrong with me and not having a diagnosis to confirm my symptoms was becoming more devastating. I began to doubt my competency as a man, a father, a husband and a physical therapist. I became more despondent as these symptoms were slowing eroding all aspects of my life. I began to feel anxious about being around other people, wondering what they were thinking about me when I would occasionally stagger, excuse myself repeatedly to go to the bathroom, or become so fatigued that I could not function. I worried about how everyone, especially my family, was reacting to me having physical problems.

Getting involved

I was pretty sure I had MS; I just didn't have any hard evidence to confirm the diagnosis. In an attempt to cope with my hypothesis I needed to retain some level of emotional stability. I needed to try to feel better about myself. In an attempt to cope with all of what was going on, I reasoned that I needed to exercise to help maintain my physical abilities. In 1979, I started swimming several times a week, but unfortunately, the availability of a pool to do lap swimming was after work and later in the evening. This meant I had to rest before I went swimming because I was fatigued from work and I wouldn't get home until after 10 PM, then get up and go to work the next morning. This translated into more time away from home, but I reasoned that several hours, three times a week didn't seem like too much! As time went on, my rationalizing the time away was reinforced as I started to feel the positive benefits of the exercise.

I also needed to know more about multiple sclerosis so I got in contact with the National Multiple Sclerosis Society for literature about the illness. They sent me a lot of information and suggested I go to the local support group, which I did. What a disaster! It was held at a nursing home and most of the people there were incapable of doing anything for themselves. The volunteers were cordial and I was warmly welcomed, but I was taken aback by the severe disability of the people who were at the meeting. Of course, in total ignorance of the disease I rapidly projected myself into their circumstance as my worst-case scenario. However, I really knew better for I had treated some patients with MS in physical therapy and they weren't all in wheelchairs and totally incapacitated.

As I learned more about the illness and realized the benefits of swimming in myself, I thought it would benefit others. I contacted the

MS Society again, but this time to volunteer to start a water exercise class for people with MS. They were excited about the proposal, for there were few aquatic programs in the state. Since I was a physical therapist and former physical education teacher they jumped at the chance to utilize my expertise and start a new program in my area. To get the program going, I contacted the Mayo Clinic Physical Therapy Program to solicit student volunteers. I received an overwhelming response; they were delighted to get some hands-on experience with people with MS in a pool setting. I contracted with the Rochester Park and Recreation Department to use their pool because it had a wheelchair ramp and the water was relatively cool. The reaction from the people with MS in the community was also great; over 20 people signed up for the program. Some people were in wheelchairs, but most could walk into the pool. The program was a success! Both the participants and the volunteer PT students gained a lot from the experience. However, I think I benefited the most, for I was using my struggle with my infirmity in a positive way. The program continued for several years, but unfortunately, we had to drop the program because of lack of pool time that was convenient for the participants. That was the end of the aquatics program in Rochester, but the beginning for me of a very long and rewarding volunteering "career" with the MS Society.

"You have multiple sclerosis" ... relief followed by grief

In 1980, I met with my fifth neurologist whom I later found was a member of the Medical Advisory Board of the National MS Society and an expert in MS. After his examination and the review of my history he proclaimed, "There is no doubt in my mind that you have multiple sclerosis."

Finally, after seven long, frustrating years of progressive symptoms; jumping from one neurologist to another; being poked and prodded with needles and reflex hammers; being probed in every orifice of my body; experiencing a decline in emotional confidence; and having my marriage slowly dissolve; I was finally diagnosed with multiple sclerosis! To my amazement I was relieved! Finally, my complaints were affirmed and my symptoms validated. I now had a label for my curse - a hook upon which I could hang my life.

I wanted to shout:

"I have multiple sclerosis!"

"That's why I'm so fatigued that I can't finish a project!"

"That's why my feet are numb and tingling!"

"That's why I stagger and fall down!"

"That's why my bladder leaks down my leg and I can't get a hard on!"

I reasoned, "It could be worse, at least it isn't a brain tumor!"

I tried to minimize the tragedy and be grateful for what I had. Denying the realism of my situation didn't last long; my relief soon turned to grief. The most powerful influence was the reality of having a chronic, progressive, debilitating disease of my central nervous system that could possibly leave me physically incapacitated and mentally incompetent. I struggled to hold myself together to keep from losing it. I worried that I would lose my job along with its financial stability. My wife stopped teaching after Grant's birth leaving her unemployed and our kids were so young; we were vulnerable. I needed to do all I could to keep my job and the benefits that came with it. I agonized over the possibility of my family having to take care of me when I was supposed to be taking care of them. I anticipated a life of disability and despair. The diagnosis didn't strengthen my marriage, but put the decline on hold for at least a little while longer. I feared what the future would hold for my family and me, but I didn't verbalize my concerns to my wife or anyone else.

I really had to tell some people that I had MS just for my own sanity and support; not everyone, just a select few who really needed to know, namely our immediate family. Unfortunately, this became another area of conflict that arose between my wife and me when she told her parents. They were, of course, very concerned and expressed their support for us. However, when I went to tell my parents I made the mistake of telling my father first. He immediately turned around and requested that I not tell my mother. He reasoned that it would cause her a major upset and he was very protective of her feelings. I respected his request because he was the one who lived with her day-to-day and he knew her very well; and he was my father whom one did not disobey. But that issue became a major point of contention with my wife because she felt it unfair that her parents knew, but my mother didn't. She was right, but I reluctantly respected my father's wishes not to tell my mother even though it caused a rift in our relationship. It was unfair to my wife and her parents not to share the grief with both of my parents. It wasn't until 1981 when I eventually told my mother. By that time my staggering and loss of balance were very noticeable and I knew she would question these obvious symptoms. When I did tell her, she was furious for not letting her know sooner.

We didn't tell our children who were now seven and five, for we didn't want them to worry; they were too young to fully understand the possible circumstances. I think they knew something was wrong because of my funny walk and stiff legged running, but they never asked me about it.

Those people outside our families who eventually found out about my MS didn't really seem to understand my plight. Maybe that was because I fought so hard to be normal and hide my problems from others who might judge. I really didn't want anyone to know I had an illness that potentially could lead to severe limitations. I was afraid they would think differently of me because I thought they might have preconceived ideas of people with the disease. Exactly what they thought was scary for me. There's a certain stigma associated with having MS, one of being mentally inept and having poor cognitive function. The medical literature tends to describe the worst-case scenario and part of that description is the inability to think, remember and make appropriate decisions. I didn't want to carry around the stigma of being incompetent.

I worked hard to hide my symptoms and was very selective with whom I shared my diagnosis outside of my family. I sought understanding from those around me, yet did not want to reveal to them that I had MS. But, in hiding the scope of my MS from my family, friends and co-workers, and trying to smooth over any problems they might think I have, I was emotionally isolating myself. I was, for the most part, non-visible with my physical problems and becoming more introverted with my emotional struggle. Yet through times of despondency and distress I wanted to shout out to anyone who would listen, "I have MS and I'm afraid!" I wanted to reach out and talk to someone just to help validate my situation. But, I wouldn't. Maybe it was a guy thing. I tended to hold onto my emotions anyway. I was very good at hiding my feelings. I was becoming the metaphor songs are written about; "I am a rock, I am an island; for a rock feels no pain and an island never cries." But in reality, I not only cried and felt pain, my spirit bled.

On occasion I was given the opportunity to share my plight, although reluctantly. One day, while walking our dog, I met our neighbor who was a nurse at the hospital. During the conversation, he noticed my abnormal walking and asked if I had a bad knee. I tried to shake off the question with a retort of, "it's an old football injury," but he was persistent with his questioning; I'm sure it was the nurse in him trying to gather more information. With his persistence to know more about my leg, I finally blurted out, "I have MS!" His face turned bright red with embarrassment and he became profusely apologetic. I told him not to be concerned, but his response reinforced my reluctance to share my dilemma.

I eventually had to tell my supervisor at work. The frequency of my fatigue and my bladder urgency were affecting my work responsibilities, plus my staggering gait was becoming more noticeable. I was afraid he and others would think I was drunk or using drugs. When I told him, he was very supportive and assured me that he was willing to make accommodations for my limitations. To protect my benefits, he suggested I inform Mayo Clinic personnel and to have them help me make necessary accommodations to my work responsibilities. Ironically, knowing that I had something going wrong with my body, I had contacted them before I was diagnosed to sign up for supplemental disability insurance. And although I haven't had the need to use it, I felt somewhat reassured of my future ability to financially support my family. Also, I was taken aback when the head of personnel said, "Whenever you decide to go on disability, let us know and we can arrange for it." I was stunned to think it would be so easy to get disability benefits. In one regard, it was reassuring to think I have that support, but on the other hand it sounded too easy to take advantage of it. I wanted to continue to work as long as possible, so I decided to fight for my right to do so. I wanted to be a productive part of society for my own self-worth, but also for the stability it provided. Being on disability would wreak financial havoc on my family.

Most of the people I worked with at the time had no clue as to my difficulties and I wasn't about to tell them because of my unresolved fears of being labeled incompetent or deficient. I also didn't want to be perceived as a complainer or whiner. But as my symptoms became more visible, I could sense that my colleagues' confidence in my abilities began to wane, as did mine. Eventually they were told of my dilemma through meetings with my supervisor. The "cat was out of the bag" and I had to deal with my perceptions of their perceptions of me. Of course, I didn't openly share my concerns; I just plugged away at my work, doing the best I could do under the circumstances. I reasoned that I needed to expend most of my physical energy at work to maintain my job, my salary and the medical benefits for my growing family; all the necessities of being the sole breadwinner. As a result, my time and energy at home diminished.

Decisions, decisions

When I was faced with the effects of fatigue on my work, I had to make some monumental decisions.

"Do I continue to work and struggle to get around as I had been?" If I did, I ran the risk of being dismissed for not being able to fulfill my employment responsibilities.

"Do I go on disability?" If I did, my family's financial security would be jeopardized.

"Do I make changes at work to accommodate my limitations?" If I did, I would expose myself to the scrutiny of my peers.

I opted to choose the latter. I would be more financially secure and emotionally fulfilled if I continued to be a productive member of society and I would be in better control of my life with MS. I enjoyed my work; I just had trouble getting from point A to point B.

To make changes that would allow me to work full time, I needed to find a way to be able to go long distances at St. Mary's Hospital, which is a very large and long complex of buildings. In my job, I had to go from one end of the hospital to other ends, sometimes 2 blocks away, many times a day. I was getting exhausted walking these distances, to say the least.

I needed to find a way of adapting to my situation and the only way short of those other options was to start using a wheelchair. That was not an easy decision. I needed to confront my emotional conflicts with admitting to myself that I had a limitation and then deal with the perceptions of everyone else's perceptions of me in a wheelchair. Seeing a physical therapist using a wheelchair seems like an oxymoron; it just doesn't seem to fit. I kept asking myself, "How will my fellow employees and my patients react to me using a wheelchair?" I didn't need the wheelchair all of the time, so trying to explain my periodic use of the wheelchair meant telling others that I had a problem. But I had to do something or I would lose my job and the financial stability it provided.

Before I started to use a wheelchair at work I explored the various options in wheelchairs that were available. With the help of another physical therapist and the encouragement of a recreational therapist who was paraplegic, I decided to use a manual wheelchair. It was more mobile – I could easily get it in and out of my car – and it fit more readily into my life's philosophy – if it's physical, it's therapy.

At first, it felt incongruous and awkward to wheel up to an area of the hospital, get out of the wheelchair, walk around treating my patients then get back in the wheelchair to go to another part of the hospital. I needed to repeat the sequence over again many times a day. I tried to hide the transition of going from sitting to being vertical; I would try to get out of the chair when no one was looking. I likened it to Clark Kent ducking around the corner to change into his alter ego, Superman. I was very self-conscious about how I looked to those who saw me in both situations, sitting in the wheelchair and walking around. I began to rationalize in my favor. I compared the whole situation to why someone uses a bicycle. If I were to ask my son to go to the corner grocery store to get a loaf of bread, he would ride his bike to the store, buy the bread, jump on his bike and ride home.

"Did he ride his bike in the store?"

"Did he ride his bike in the house?"

No, of course not! He went from point A to point B, did his thing and then went back to point A, quickly and efficiently. That's how I justified using my wheelchair, getting to point B. My wheelchair gets me to where I need to go, saves my energy, and permits me to maintain my job, my dignity and my life.

I have heard other people with MS say they don't want to use a wheelchair because they don't want to be confined to it. I understand their thinking because I once had the same attitude. But, my fears of being a prisoner to the wheelchair or giving into the disease were dispelled once I started to use one. On the contrary, I had feelings of freedom; I was granted a reprieve from being overburdened from fatigue. The ease of movement and maintaining my independence were exhilarating sensations!

Some years later, this issue came up for discussion in the support group I was leading. One of the participants, a woman in her mid-forties with moderate limitations of mobility, stated emphatically, "I will *never* use a wheelchair. I don't want to be confined to it." I asked her how she did her grocery or Christmas shopping. She exclaimed, "Either my husband or my kids do those things for me because I get too fatigued!" She further explained that she stays at home most of the time because she gets too fatigued to go out for any reason. In other words, she "confined" herself to her home to prevent getting fatigued. Yet, she didn't want to use a wheelchair, which would allow her the freedom to move about because she didn't want to be "confined to a wheelchair!"

Ironically, there was a gentleman in the same group who shared with us his recent early retirement from his job. He went on disability because his employment responsibilities involved walking around a large complex of buildings, supervising the work; and this caused him to become overwhelmingly fatigued. His company was willing to purchase a wheelchair for him, which would have permitted him to fulfill his responsibilities and stay employed, but he was intimidated by what he thought his co-workers would think of him and how they would react. He didn't want to be thought of as being a slacker or viewed as being lazy. In reality, he went on disability because he didn't want to be labeled as disabled.

I asked both participants, "What would you do if you were to win an all-expense paid trip to Disney World for you and your family? Would you go?"

They both responded with an, "Of course!"

I then asked, "How would you get around?"

They both answered, "I'd have to use a wheelchair."

I then asked, "You just got through telling us that you didn't want to use a wheelchair at home, why would you be willing to use one at Disney World?"

The woman said, "No one knows me at Disney World!" The gentleman agreed.

That story emphasizes the importance of perceptions. Both of the support group participants didn't want to be perceived as being "confined to a wheelchair" or as being "disabled." This perception prevented them from managing their fatigue with an adaptive device, the wheelchair. This perception of being confined to a wheelchair or being disabled influenced my contemplation of managing fatigue with a wheelchair. There were two perceptions involved for me; the perception I had of myself and the perception of others' perceptions of me in the wheelchair. I chose to ignore whatever people thought.

Make no mistake; my fatigue didn't miraculously go away just because I started using a wheelchair. The potential for fatigue was still there, but the wheelchair gave me some resolution to my limits. I had to make a choice when I was confronted with using a wheelchair to manage my fatigue; either I use a wheelchair or I don't work. I chose the former. I couldn't afford not to work, not only financially but also psychologically. However, there were some downsides to using a wheelchair in the beginning. I felt good about my decision to start using a wheelchair at work. But, the reaction from those around me, at first, varied from confusion, to suspicion, to consternation. The majority of my physical therapy colleagues were very supportive because they understood my needs. Most everyone else said nothing. I would get an occasional inquisitive query such as, "Didn't I just see you in a wheelchair?" Or, "Didn't I just see you walking around?" However, some of those I worked around were, frankly, downright rude. Being confronted with comments like "you're faking it" or "what a lazy way to get around" were difficult to take, to say the least. Those people really ticked me off! Here I'm trying to tame this wild beast, fatigue, and they're standing there ridiculing me for trying. They had no right to judge me when they didn't even know what I was about or what circumstances I lived under. I could only try to ignore their biting comments and glaring stares.

More trouble at home

For the most part, I could do all the normal things fathers, husbands and physical therapists do: help care for the kids, love my wife, work around the house and go to the hospital to treat patients. However, as my fatigue became more pronounced, my ability to do these things as efficiently as possible began to diminish. It took me longer to do chores and work-related activities because I needed to rest for short periods. I didn't feel sleepy or weak, just fatigued. It was as if I had a cold or the flu. I could become fully drained of energy, yet I didn't feel sick. I started to put things off because it became physically burdensome to do everything on my to-do list. Since it took me longer to finish what I started, unfinished tasks began to pile up. I began to limit how I would expend my energy and I reasoned that my need to keep my job and support my family took priority over other responsibilities at home. This put a great burden on me to keep my job and an even greater burden on my wife to take up the slack at home.

Of course, my wife saw my ups and downs even when I tried to hide them. On occasion, we would talk about my symptoms, but neither one of us had a clue as to when these things would occur. Although she was sympathetic at first, the diagnosis of MS didn't do anything to strengthen our relationship and it was beginning to drive an emotional wedge between us. We lacked the skills to deal with the enormity of the situation and even though we had opportunities to seek psychological help, I ignored or refused them thinking we could handle the problem on our own.

I was the major contributor to this benign neglect; I thought it would be ok, that things would work their way out on their own and they did, but unfortunately, to the negative. In retrospect, the choices I made, of course, were wrong, but the proverbial hindsight is 20/20.

As the years passed and the symptoms progressed, it became more apparent that these were becoming a permanent part of my life. I became more worried about my future. The greater my worry, the more I withdrew into myself; my disposition became more solemn. At times, fatigue fogged my consciousness, which fed the remorse regarding my physical decline. I worried about not being able to run and play with my kids and do other "fatherly" activities with them. I worried about not being the husband I was supposed to be and had fears that my wife would leave me for a more capable man. My future role as a parent and spouse looked dim, but I still didn't share my concerns. The stoic and so-called "macho, silence-is-strength" concept was self-defeating. The relationship between my wife and me continued to weaken. More specific symptoms drove the wedge deeper between us.

Incontinence of my bladder was becoming more frequent and, on occasion, I would have an accident with my bowels. To wake up in the middle of the night soiled in your own feces and urine was horrifying and extremely embarrassing! My bowel incontinence happened only once at night, but I had several bladder episodes. They were infrequent and unpredictable. My wife seemed empathetic, but I could sense it was worrying her more than she was verbally sharing. These symptoms would diminish intimacy between any two people. These were disturbing events and I became extremely afraid to go anywhere or be too far from a bathroom. Just in case of an emergency, I began to calculate the distance to the nearest bathroom and how long it might take me to get there. As I focused my attention on avoiding an accident, these bowel and bladder issues began to consume more of my mental energy. Whenever I had any kind of urge to go, I would immediately look for a bathroom. It could be in the middle of a conversation, working with a patient or driving the car; when I felt the need to go I would head for the nearest toilet. I was so afraid of having an accident; I assumed every little bowel or bladder sensation would end in disaster. However, more often than not, these sensations were false alarms. I became frustrated when I would get to a bathroom and nothing happened. But, the further I got from a bathroom, the more anxiety I would have about getting back to it! As expected, the closer I got to a bathroom, the less anxious I would be.

The sequence of feeling a need to go, running to the bathroom and not being able to go, started to wear me down, physically and emotionally. To gain some kind of control, I would try to manipulate my environment to better my odds of not having an accident. I made a point of knowing where the closest bathrooms were before going to a meeting, a restaurant or movie theater and I would situate myself as close to the exit as possible so I could get up and go at a moment's notice. I also prayed that when I got to my "sanctuary of relief," it wouldn't be occupied. I would anticipate escape routes and excuses in case I didn't make it on time. I felt out of control, my bladder and bowels were controlling my life.

One of the most frustrating, feeling-out-of-control situations was when I was flying in an airplane. There are two times during the flight when I felt totally afraid of having an accident; taking off and landing. During those portions of the flight, I couldn't just jump up and get to the toilet. While being confined to my seat "with my seatbelt securely fastened," I was more afraid of losing control of my bowels than I was of being in an airplane crash. I would agonize over each trip I took. I would make sure I had an aisle seat as close to the bathrooms as possible and even endured sitting in the smoking section of the plane just to be close to the toilet. I was taking many flights every year because of my work, so I had to endure these tortuous moments often.

When I was riding in a car, I felt I was in a little more control as long as I was driving. I would deliberately offer to drive alone, making up some lame excuse about maybe leaving early or whatever I could think of at the time. I figured if I were alone I would just go home and clean myself up or I could always just pull over and go in the bushes. Of course, that wasn't possible driving in the city, so I don't know what would have happened if I weren't alone.

The one time that something did happen, I was with Greta; fortunately, she was just six months old. We were on our way home from the grocery store and she was crying and fussing because she had a dirty diaper. All of a sudden I had the threatening urge to go; we were far from home with no gas stations or restaurants in sight. An explosion soon followed my urge, but fortunately, I was able pull over and get out of the car just in time before soiling myself. I was devastated! It was extremely humiliating to be incontinent, but to do so in front of my daughter even if she was only a baby was even more distressing. I was able to cover the seat with some plastic I had in the car, so I got back in and headed home with the both of us in messy, smelly pants. Fortunately, my wife wasn't home when we arrived, so of course, I first attended to Greta who was crying even more intensely. A cacophony of crying erupted as I joined in with her intense bawling. We "serenaded" each other the whole time while I was cleaning her up. After I got her cleaned up and settled down in her bassinet with a bottle of her mother's milk and a well-powdered behind, I then had to go and clean myself up. What a mess! I was afraid my wife would come home and find my predicament, so I had to move quickly to shower, throw my evidence in the washing machine then disinfect and deodorize everything in sight. Fortunately, I didn't have another episode of that nature in front of my daughter or anyone else, but I agonized over the conundrum of being the parent helping my children with toilet training, when I couldn't even control my own bodily functions!

The abyss widens

With all the symptoms, lack of communication and stresses of life in general, my wife and I were drifting apart. However, the biggest wedge that was driven into the heart of our relationship was my increased sexual impotence. Our marriage wasn't built around exotic sexual escapades in the bedroom, but the emotional trauma of loss of intimacy was horrendous to each other's self-esteem and to our relationship. The more often I failed, the more damage to my self image and my self worth; the greater the divide between us. She thought she was the reason I couldn't "get it up." She didn't think she was attractive enough for me to be visually stimulated! I tried to reassure her that I loved her and she was not the cause of the impotence, but unfortunately, my lack of physical response with attempts at lovemaking did not support my verbal appeal for her. Lack of satisfaction and fear of failure led to diminished intimacy and broadened the abyss between us.

Chapter Two

The Story Continues... From Victim to Survivor

As I told it over and over, I came to realize I was living my life through my story and I had become a victim of it. When I stopped living my story, I became a survivor!

As one door closes, another opens

I didn't heed the continued warnings of withdrawal I was receiving from my wife. Our relationship continued to erode. The physical issues of bladder and bowel incontinence, sexual impotence and bouts of severe fatigue were coupled with bilateral emotional withdrawal from our relationship. We both ignored the red flags of despair being raised from both sides of our bed. Attempts to establish any level of normalcy in my life had failed. I tried to live normally, be married, raise a family and pursue a career. It seemed as though multiple sclerosis was robbing me of these pleasures, but in reality it wasn't the MS that was the thief, it was my reaction to the disease that stole the "me" from my "self."

When, in 1981, my wife proclaimed her intentions of divorce, I pleaded with her to reconcile. I begged her to go to counseling with me. She agreed to go, but it was to no avail. Even after three weeks of intense psychotherapy, she was determined to follow through with the divorce. I was an emotional wreck. My body was rebelling against me and my wife was leaving me; my family was being ripped apart and I was headed toward financial disaster. A year later, the divorce was finalized and I was further devastated with the reality of my deteriorating life.

Within two years of my diagnosis, I was divorced, depressed and in grave despair. I was overwhelmed with the rejection of my body and my wife. With all this devastation in my life, I just existed, barely at times, but I was alive! With the help of continued group psychotherapy and the resolve to maintain my fatherhood as normally as possible I was able to move on. I loved my children and fought to be with them as much as possible even though they were only with me on weekends. Their love kept me going through the emotional hell in which I found myself.

Moving on

My neurologist was retiring and recommended a new member of the staff to take over my treatment. He was new to the Mayo Clinic but was not new to MS; he was a world-renowned expert! He was fantastic, very thorough in his assessment of my status with MS and very frank with my options, which were to live my life to the fullest despite my situation.

His encouragement helped me to seek outlets for my frustrations with the disease and the divorce, and I soon found release through wheelchair sports. The recreational therapist who helped me getting my first wheelchair for work encouraged me to try road racing and basketball. I didn't realize I was even eligible to participate in these sports. I thought I had to be paralyzed and unable to walk. I discovered as long as I had a diagnosis and a limitation in mobility I was qualified. Unfortunately, because I was able to get out of my wheelchair and walk about, albeit with a stiff-legged stagger and an occasional stumble, some of the other disabled athletes who couldn't get up and walk because of their paralysis occasionally shunned me. It didn't happen with everyone, but there were a few who thought I wasn't disabled enough to be in "their league." That bothered me at first, but then I realized it was their problem with their disability, not me with mine. I was able to look beyond that narrow-mindedness to the positives I was getting out of the activities. Ironically, after telling one of the paraplegic ballplayers I had MS, he empathetically responded, "I'm glad I don't have what you have!"

I felt good participating in any athletic activity, even if it was using a wheelchair. The skill of maneuvering a wheelchair in such sports has continued to benefit me during everyday use. My ability to "pop wheelies," open doors and develop upper body strength prepared me to successfully challenge physical and emotional inaccessibility.

No sweat

Playing wheelchair sports helped me to cope with my illness. It not only improved my physical fitness, but I learned more about my fatigue, which has had the greatest influence on my life; it is immense. I always thought of fatigue as a solitary entity but I came to learn that with MS it is a conglomerate of complex components; each with its different influences; each with its own temperament; and each with its own prejudices and biases. For me to successfully manage this symptom, I needed to have a thorough understanding of each part, the "pieces of the pie," as it were, and how each affects the sum total. My experience at the beach years previously was an example of one of those aspects of fatigue and MS; increased body temperature causes fatigue. I eventually found this is one of the most common symptoms experienced by people with MS.

I became acutely aware of another one of these "pieces of pie" during one of our wheelchair basketball games when the coach called a time out. As we gathered around him at the bench, I noticed all of the other players were asking the manager to throw them a towel to wipe the sweat from their bodies. It was then I realized I didn't need a towel because I wasn't sweating! I had been playing almost an entire game of basketball and I was dry as a bone. I used to sweat like the proverbial pig! Of course, it wasn't until I moved to Minnesota that I later learned pigs don't actually sweat, so in reality I was now really sweating like a pig!

Soon after my historic revelation about not being able to sweat, I mentioned this phenomenon to my neurologist. He thought it wise to get this checked out and documented. So, he sent me to the "thermoregulatory lab" in the bowels of one of the buildings at the Mayo Clinic. It was there that they could measure how much someone can sweat. And did they ever try. The technician covered my almost naked body with an orange powder that turns purple when it comes in contact with water. They then put me a large baker, an oven of sorts, at a temperature of 114 degrees. After about 20 minutes they took me out of the oven and took a picture of me with a digital camera and then fed the image into a computer that calculated the area of purple and compared it to the area of orange left on my body. I had only 12% of purple showing, a little on my brow, some under my arms and along the front of my chest. Other than that, I was dry as a bone and orange! The test showed that I truly had lost my sweat response. The big drawback of the test however, was that I was wiped out from getting too hot. Fortunately, I was able to take a shower - a cool shower. As my original body tints were being restored, it was like watching some weird science fiction movie. I saw my orange body turn into purple streaks as the powder washed down the drain. It did cool me down though!

Not being able to sweat has few advantages and is trouble for the most part. Sweating is the normal way of helping to keep the body cool. As the sweat evaporates, it helps to dissipate the heat from the surface of the body. Without sweating, my body temperature can rise to dangerous, life-threatening levels. So, what do I do to compensate for not sweating? While I was playing basketball, I tried spraying my skin with a mixture of rubbing alcohol and water in order to mimic sweating. That didn't work. I tried taking a cold shower during half-time, which helped a little, but it consumed too much time and energy, as well as being inconvenient. What really worked best was drinking large amounts of ice water during breaks in the game. Of course, drinking a lot of water has its drawbacks; what goes in, must come out and it was the coming out that became the problem. I had to tell the coach, "If you suddenly see me leave the game, it's not because I fouled out. I just need to quickly get to a bathroom and I'm not waiting for a time out!"

Channeling MS in positive ways

I found solace volunteering with the MS Society and became heavily involved with many activities. Because of my experience as a patient in psychotherapy I became intrigued with the small group process of helping people solve problems. But, I wanted to be on the other side of the table and lead a group! I met another person with MS, Constance, who was finishing her master's degree in Counseling and was interested in starting an MS support group. We teamed up and launched a new group for people who were newly-diagnosed or mildly affected. It was a huge success; we had over 25 people who would regularly come to the monthly meetings.

Because of my previous experience running Rochester's former aquatics program, the MS Society asked me if I would be interested in helping them again with a new program at the MS Camp held annually. I jumped at the chance and later that year, after soliciting help from the Mayo's Physical Therapy Program, brought five PT students with me to MS Camp to run the water exercise program. It was also a huge success! The students received the benefit of hands-on contact with people with MS and the campers were the recipients of energized students willing to share their new learned skills.

I wanted even more involvement and soon found myself on several Minnesota MS Society committees and was eventually appointed to the Board of Trustees. At the same time, I became involved with several national, state and alumni physical therapy association boards and committees. In addition, I was appointed to the Minnesota Governor's Council on Disability. These activities were very rewarding; they gave me the opportunity to take advantage of my skills as a physical therapist and a person with a disability. I was involved with these activities, all while seeing Greta and Grant on weekends; working full-time; playing wheelchair basketball; dating; and coping with the progression of my MS.

All of my activities did not go unnoticed. Within two years I was presented with the Minnesota MS Society's Volunteer of the Year and the Outstanding Achievement Awards, as well as the Mayo PT Program's Outstanding Alumnus Award. In 1986, I was a recipient of the National MS Society's Area V Achievement Award - one of only five in the nation!

Helping others deal with their problems helped me with mine. Working with other people with MS as a volunteer was very rewarding and gave me strength. I was at the peak of maximizing my potential with MS while minimizing my disability. I was no longer a victim; I was living my life the way I wanted, in spite of my MS. I was becoming a survivor! But, I needed greater fulfillment and I realized I might be able to help even more people by melding my personal and volunteer experiences with MS with my physical therapy career. In 1986, I transferred from working in the ICU, to working in the Rehabilitation Unit, exclusively treating patients with MS. It was there where I really felt I was using my MS in the most positive way. It all seemed to come together. My patients benefited from my expertise as a PT, a volunteer with the MS Society and as a person with MS. I also learned more about how other people with MS dealt with their disease, which in turn helped me to deal with my MS. I felt right at home among colleagues who understood adaptation to a disability while modeling the result of rehabilitation for patients who were in need of the concept. This furthered my expertise in dealing with my illness, so the more I gave of myself, the more I learned about myself!

A new chapter in my life

After the divorce, I began to date despite my fears of how others might feel with my having an illness like MS. Fortunately, my symptoms were still mostly non-visible so I looked and moved relatively normal most of the time. However, during these times of positive exploits, I continued to deal with my bodily dysfunction. I longed to be part of a family and since I couldn't be married to the mother of my children, I wanted to re-establish a nuclear family. Of course, the only way to do that would be to marry someone who had children. I managed to survive through several long relationships until I finally met someone whom I thought understood the fluctuations of my disease and the emotionally-related adjustments. In 1987, I married Barb and ventured into an extended family. Although I gained the love of four wonderful stepchildren, it seemed to be at the expense of my relationship with my own children. Unfortunately, that attempt to regain normalcy in my life only led to their separation from me. My attempt to smooth out my life and blend my new family with my children failed miserably and led to more turmoil. I was feeling very guilty for the damage to my family for which I thought I was responsible. My repeated attempts to reconnect with Greta and Grant were only met with resistance. Little did I know that a big contributor to that conflict was their stepfather, who was undermining our relationship for his own benefit. It wasn't until almost ten years later his deceitfulness was exposed.

With the added energy and time involved with my new larger family, I had to give up most of my activities with the MS Society and the physical therapy associations. Unfortunately, my wheelchair sports activities were also suspended. I replaced the emotional and physical benefits I received from them with the gain of family life, the latter of which had been a big void in my life. My MS was stable at the time and I felt I could manage the change in lifestyle. Despite the separation from my children, my new family was supportive of me with my MS. Plus, the physical nature of helping raise four children was a different form of exercise.

MS strikes again

Beginning in 1990, I embarked on one of the toughest challenges of my life. Over a period of approximately one year, I developed pain in my right side that was indicative of a rapid progression of a severe abnormal curvature of my spine, known as scoliosis. My MS had caused weakness of muscles on one side of my back and tightness of the muscles on the other side. This caused my spine to twist and curl to one side, which caused pain, and affected my posture and my walking. The orthopedic surgeon who was following my case, warned me of a potentially life-threatening situation in which the twisting of my spine and chest wall would cause compression of my heart and lungs. I started exercising again in an attempt to halt the progression of the scoliosis. My neurologist thought a series of intravenous steroids would help, but neither the exercise nor very strong medication helped to stem the progression of the scoliosis. Over a period of a year, my spine went from 12 degrees of bending and twisting to 57 degrees!

The only recourse was to have most of my spine fused with metal rods and bone grafts. I was devastated with the thought of extensive surgery and the long recuperation afterward. I asked myself:

"How would this affect my physical abilities, my family and my job?"

"Would the surgery cause my MS to worsen?"

"Would I be able to go back to work and if I couldn't, how would I support my family?"

All these questions and more were unanswerable and I had no choice; either risk the hazards of surgery and the possibility of complications or run the future risk of having more pain along with heart and lung damage from the scoliosis. The other concern was how the surgery would be performed. If I had the surgery right away the orthopedic surgeon would fuse my spine from the back. If I waited, he would have to cut open my chest and abdomen to fuse the front part of my spine, which had more serious risks and longer recuperation. I chose not to wait and elected to have the surgery as soon as possible. I had the greatest confidence in the surgeon's skill; this type of surgery was his specialty.

I tried to prepare for this big event. I contacted my kids and met with them to explain my situation and concerns, but they weren't at all supportive. But under the circumstances with their stepfather, I don't blame them. I tried to get in the best physical shape possible through a vigorous physical therapy program for more strengthening and endurance exercises. I even arranged to have some of my blood drawn and stored before the surgery.

In October of 1992, after 14 hours on the operating table to fuse my spine from just below my neck all the way down to the end, I awoke in the intensive care unit on a ventilator connected to a tube in my throat, IVs in my arms, tubes stuck in practically every other orifice of my body and my back on fire! The surgery was a success, but the aftereffects were overwhelming! I had to be given massive amounts of blood during the surgery, 20 units to be exact, and was quite anemic afterward. Several more units of blood were required to stabilize my blood pressure after surgery. In the end, I received 23 units of blood. Once I got off the ventilator and had the breathing tube removed, I moved out of the ICU and into a room on the orthopedic nursing unit. I started my rehabilitation, which was very slow at first. I had a long way to go before I could go home. I required narcotics to control my post-operative pain and had an IV hooked up to a morphine pump, which allowed me to periodically administer my own pain medication. It's a great device! Having pain? Push a button, no pain! Of course, there were limits as to how much I could receive, but it sure saved the nurses a lot of steps and me a lot of needle sticks. Unfortunately, the major drawback to receiving narcotics like morphine is that it shuts down everything, namely intestinal peristalsis. I had a tube through my nose down into my stomach to prevent the build-up of fluids. I couldn't have it removed and get something to eat until I no longer needed morphine and I could pass gas.

As I was weaned from the morphine, the nurse started to hear bowel sounds with her stethoscope so she pulled the tube and ordered a meal. Ah, the taste of food after five days was a wonderful blessing! This eventually led to more of a curse than a blessing, for an inevitable result of my eating was the need to start using a commode. This meant I needed to get up out bed, which was quite a trick since I had to wear a plastic body jacket with a leg extension to prevent me from bending at the waist. This "turtle shell" was used to allow time for the fusion to harden and turn my spine into a solid mass. The only time I was allowed to bend at the waist by unlocking the leg piece was when I sat on the commode.

To get out of bed without being able to bend through my spine and waist was arduous, painful and time consuming. At first, I needed a lot of help from the nurses. What a production! It took three nurses to support my leg, turn my body and prevent me from toppling over. The first time I stood, I almost passed out because my blood pressure dropped precipitously. The nurses had to reverse the procedure very quickly or I would have been on the floor! Over time, with multiple attempts to stand and a final unit of hemoglobin to help increase my blood volume, I was able to stand without passing out. I also had more and more of the tubes and IVs taken out of my body, which freed me from those inconveniences. Unfortunately, I still needed to have my bladder periodically emptied with a catheter and I had to learn how to do this by myself before I went home.

I eventually learned to manipulate my hospital bed and my body to be able to stand by myself at my bedside. I was then ready to go to physical therapy for exercise and to learn to walk while wearing the body brace. Ironically, I went to the very Rehab Unit where I worked as a therapist just before my surgery. I was now the patient and my colleagues were my therapists. I felt odd at first, but I knew I was in good hands.

I spent a total of three weeks in the hospital recuperating from all the effects of anesthesia, loss of blood, pain and fatigue from the MS and weakness from immobility. When I was discharged, I had lost over 25 pounds; I was weak, tired very quickly and needed help with activities of daily living - dressing, eating and moving about. I needed a hospital bed at home to be able to get in and out of bed and I had to stand to eat because of the leg extension on the body jacket. This meant propping one hip up on a stool while standing on the other. To shower, my wife had to help get my body jacket off and on, which was quite an ordeal. I wore a t-shirt underneath that needed to be removed before I showered. So, we removed the body jacket, took off the t-shirt, and then put the body jacket on again. I would then use a walker to go to the shower. Afterward, I had to get back in bed to take the jacket off. She would dry the body jacket with a hair dryer and then help me put on a clean t-shirt and the dry body jacket. I was so exhausted afterward I would have to take a nap! Fortunately, I didn't have to shower everyday. But I did have to catheterize my bladder 3-4 times a day for several months before I could void without assistance.

To help me get stronger, I had a physical therapist come in and help with exercises and walking. Eventually, I was able to be independent with my activities of daily living and exercise. The only thing I couldn't do was drive my car, which was very frustrating.

Over the next three months my physical strength and endurance gradually returned. When I was ready to shed the body jacket, I was able to go back to work. However, I had many physical restrictions that needed accommodation. I definitely couldn't treat patients on the Rehab Unit, because it was hard work even for an able-bodied therapist. This meant I had to change jobs or go on full-time disability, the latter of which was not a viable option. Fortunately, I was able to transfer to the Hand Therapy Center to treat patients with shoulder, elbow, wrist and hand problems. Most of them were able to walk in and out of the therapy area and I was able to treat them from my wheelchair, if need be. So, despite the time and turmoil of surgery and recuperation, I still had a job!

Here I go again

Unfortunately, the ordeal of the surgery, the progression of my MS and my wife's emotional withdrawal drove her to make a decision about our relationship. In 1994, seven years after my second marriage and two years after my surgery, I again found myself divorced and further rejected. That was a tough year for me; I got divorced, my extended family moved away, my daughter distanced herself even farther from me, and I had to sell my large, vibrant home and move into a small, stagnant condominium. To make matters worse, several of the rods in my lower back broke after I fell one too many times. My falls were rather dramatic; I couldn't bend because of the spinal fusion so I must have looked like a big tree falling to the ground! As a result of the broken rods, I had to have another surgery on my back to remove the hardware and repack the bony fusion. However, the final insult of that year was when the IRS audited me! Ha! And my doctors had told me to avoid stress!

Despite the emotional, physical and financial trauma of that year, I survived. Over the next six years, I slowly rebuilt my life. I re-established a positive relationship with my son. I started to take better care of my physical and emotional needs. I moved into an all-accessible townhouse, made some changes in my career and became more active in the MS Society. I continued to work in Hand Therapy, but I also started working in Patient Education helping develop materials for the Physical Therapy Department. It was a nice career fit. I contacted the MS Society and started volunteering at MS Camp again, started a new support group and was asked to help coordinate other support groups in my area. I began to help train new support groups across the state of Minnesota and soon found myself on various committees including the Board of Trustees again. I also got involved with several physical therapy association committees. The only activity I didn't resume was wheelchair sports because of my extensive back surgery. I continued to exercise but not to the degree of intensity enjoyed before my surgery.

Again, my activities with the MS Society and the physical therapy groups did not go unnoticed. In 1997, I was honored with the National MS Society's Area II Outstanding Achievement Award and the Minnesota Chapter's Norman Cohn "Hope Award" Volunteer of the Year. That same year I was presented with the Minnesota Physical Therapy Association's Outstanding Service Recognition Award. However, the most prestigious event I could ever imagine occurred in 1999 during a black-tie-tuxedo ceremony when I was inducted into the National MS Society's Volunteer Hall of Fame at their Annual Conference in Anaheim, California. What an honor it was to be recognized by my peers in both the MS and physical therapy communities!

With all my activities I could do in spite of having MS, I came to realize that my blessings far outweighed my misfortunes. I became more aware of how fortunate I was in having an illness with such a slow progression; working in a profession at a medical center that permitted me to adapt my career within the limits of my disease; and living in a state that is a leader in the MS community.

Throughout the struggle of it all, I grew as a result of the many experiences and continued to prevail as a result of my core values of believing in and being responsible for myself. I learned to cope in more positive ways based on the lessons I learned through living with the trials and tribulations of MS, surgery, divorce and life. However, my learning wasn't over.

Chapter Three

The Never-Ending Story... From Survivor to Conqueror

As I learned to react positively to life <u>in spite of</u> my illness, I eventually became a survivor. However, when I began living my life proactively <u>because</u> of my illness, I became a conqueror!

A revelation unfolds

The most positive advancement in my learning to cope with multiple sclerosis occurred in 2000, which actually started with getting the flu. To mark my 57th birthday, I developed a very high fever, became dehydrated, and because of my intolerance to increased body temperature, became totally incapacitated, stuck in my bathroom and unable to move. Fortunately, having just bought a cell phone, I called 911 and found myself being rescued from the confines of my porcelain throne by several burly first responders. I'm sure the ambulance ride to the Emergency Room seemed anticlimactic for them compared to the more spectacular rescues these men were used to, but to me it was a blessing. However, I felt pretty pathetic as I was admitted to the hospital and placed on intravenous fluids to re-hydrate me. I hadn't taken care of myself; I was ill prepared for this possibility and the more I reflected about the scenario, the faster I sank into despair. I felt very vulnerable and actually embarrassed! I can't count how many times I had advised patients to be prepared for situations like the one I was experiencing; I had failed to take my own advice. But, as I reflected upon the circumstances that led up to my hospitalization, I knew I needed to concentrate on getting home in better shape than when I came in.

After half a day of fluids and antibiotics, my kidneys kicked in and I began to pee every half hour. I felt better as the fever subsided, but I was stiff, weak and fatigued from the whole ordeal, and not ready to go home. I was getting physical therapy to help keep my legs from getting too rigid, but it wasn't enough to get me back to my independence. My bladder dysfunction was also an issue that needed attention, so my admitting physicians suggested I be transferred; ironically, to the very same rehabilitation unit I had worked in 10 years prior. This was another dent to my ego and a further source of embarrassment. I sank further into despair.

The consequences of this episode started a cascade of events in my life that eventually led to an epiphany of sorts, which radically changed my attitude towards the future. Up until this point I had been in a reactive mode of living with MS. Granted, I had made some futuristic decisions, such as obtaining supplemental disability insurance before I was diagnosed, signing up for long-term care insurance when my employer offered it and moving into an accessible townhouse. But for the most part, I had made changes in my lifestyle when things happened to me, not because I had anticipated them. Being hospitalized because of a high fever and ending up in a Rehab Unit due to deconditioning, changed my life forever. One of my former students, who became my physical therapist while in the Rehab Unit, helped me to mold a different philosophy. As he worked with me through the exercises and treatments, I started to develop an attitude of proactivity toward my MS rather than reactivity. It was the beginning of a more aggressive approach toward my MS - something I had envisioned several times before, but had never put forth any effort into adopting. With his help, I tried various exercise machines and techniques to increase my endurance, strength and flexibility. He took me down to the hospital's Healthy Living Center for employees to explore the accessibility of a "health club" environment. However, the inaccessibility of the gym was more of an emotional barrier than a physical one. I usually didn't have an issue of other people's perception of me in a wheelchair; however, a health club brought to mind images of "hard bodies" in muscles shirts or workout tights. It was not a place where a 50-something-year-old man in a wheelchair would workout -- at least that was the perception I needed to overcome. Perception aside, I joined the Rochester Athletic Club, which was more physically-accessible than the employee gym and had a swimming pool. When I went to the athletic club to workout I found my perception was somewhat askew. Yes, there were many young hard bodies, but there were also a lot of individuals my age who were in just as bad of shape as I was, and they didn't use a wheelchair! This actually boosted my morale. Given my competitive nature, I found myself silently competing with other men my age and, for the most part, I was winning! However, I was also competing against the benign neglect I had inflicted on my body and I had a long way to go!

The hospitalization shook my confidence, but the overall experience triggered my motivation to exercise. Unfortunately, there were challenges beyond perceptions. Fatigue was the biggest obstacle. I needed to incorporate exercise into my daily routine without compromising my work responsibilities. My basic workday was from 8 a.m. to 5 p.m., with an hour for lunch. However there were many busy days when I spent 9-10 hours getting the work done, which usually left me very fatigued! Just thinking of exercising after work was tiring. The best time of day for me energy-wise was in the morning, so I started going to the athletic club at 6 a.m. An hour to workout, a half hour to shower and another half hour to get to work on time, three times a week became a comfortable routine, at least for a while. My exercise routine became easier as I got into better shape and I chose not to maintain that easy schedule, it's not in my nature. I began increasing my exercises to accommodate my needs and found myself getting up at 4:30 a.m. to get to the gym by opening time at 5 a.m.

Challenge accepted

As I exercised, I gained strength, endurance and overall function, but their levels were mediocre compared to what would occur two years later. In 2002, the Minnesota Chapter of the MS Society announced it was going to sponsor a 50-Mile Challenge Walk to raise funds for MS. I was moved by the thought of somehow completing 50 miles over three days to raise money for research that would potentially cure and reverse my disease. But I couldn't walk 50 feet! I had some experience with short Walks using my wheelchair, but 50 miles? No way! I had heard of people using a handcycle, a three-wheeled wheelchair that is propelled by using the arms to "crank" the front wheel through a series of gears like a bicycle, but I had never used one myself. I was able to find one I could borrow for a week or two, but after my first trial run I felt as if my arms were going to fall off and I had only gone a mile! However, the sensation of moving my body through space was invigorating and after several runs of increased distance and decreased arm fatigue I could feel the training take effect, so I accepted the challenge and signed up for the event. However, the challenge wasn't only physical; it was a fundraising event and each participant needed to raise a minimum of $1500, much more than I had ever raised before. But that didn't dissuade me from my goal of participating in and completing the Walk. I purchased a used handcycle and started training. After training and fundraising hard over the next five months, I completed the 50 miles with over $4000 in pledges! I was tired, but it felt great! The Walk itself was inspiring; over 300 people accepted and completed the challenge and I felt as if they did it for me. The enthusiasm and spirit was contagious.

When the MS Society announced it would have the Walk again in 2003, I immediately signed up. Again, to train for the 50 miles and raise the $1500 minimum was challenging, but I was determined to accept it. I continued to exercise over the winter at the athletic club, but not at the intensity that would make a difference. The 2003 Walk was a repeat of the previous one; I raised the money, completed the walk, and again felt tired.

It wasn't until after the third year of sponsoring the Walk that I experienced a revelation. In my winter training program I focused on exercises that would help me to complete the Walk and did so with a high concentration of cross-training activities. My strength and endurance improved overall and I noticed the training effect was spilling over into the rest of my life. Training for the Walk had become a year-round endeavor and helped to improve my day-to-day function.

Another light goes on

In 2004, I had another revelation. After listening to an MS research update, it became apparent to me that I could be alive when the cause, cure and reversal of MS are made available. Barring any other catastrophes, I may fully realize the true magnitude of having MS eradicated from my being! What a revelation! It may be possible for me to walk without assistance; be free from fatigue, stiffness, numbness and other MS symptoms. These have been a part my life for such a long time and now there was a strong possibility for me to be rid of this burden.

Well, easier said than done. There are many things that have to happen, but the possibilities are present to find the cause, cure and reversal of symptoms - it will just take more time and money. The technology and research design is in place and closer than ever for these breakthroughs to occur. That is where the 50-Mile Challenge Walk fit into the picture. The challenge of the event was to be physically prepared to complete the course and to raise the money, a significant amount of which goes to research. This was parallel to my goal of ridding my life of MS. The Walk became a metaphor by highlighting the need for me to be physically prepared for the cure and reversal of the disease and continue to raise money to support the research that would conquer this illness! With these concepts in mind and a determination to be as fit as possible, I completed the 2004, 2005 and the 2006 Walks. I continue to train for future Walks with the same enthusiasm dedicated to preparing myself for a future free from MS.

These changes in my life prompted me to make a monumental jump of faith in the future. In January of 2006, after a 33 1/2-year career in physical therapy, I retired from the Mayo Clinic! The main incentives in my decision were to expend more energy on exercise and devote more time to volunteering. There were so many times I had to stop working out and go to work even though I had the energy to continue. There were also times when my work would interfere with my volunteer efforts with the MS Society, which had expanded to include service on national committees. When I found I was financially stable enough to retire, I jumped at the opportunity! My career goal was to retire before I had to go on disability and I finally reached it. It was a feel-good decision; being a retired 63-year-old physical therapist with MS has a nice ring to it! It feels great to have the time and energy to pursue my new life's career goal; to prepare my body, mind and spirit for the cure and reversal of MS!

My story doesn't end here; it really just begins. Although there is the possibility of a new life free from MS, my struggle continues day-to-day, step-by-step until my new beginning arrives. I still have to contend with the adversities associated with living with a chronic, progressive, debilitating illness.

Chapter Four

I Have a Gift...

It is not adversity that builds character, it's the way we manage it that determines the nature of our being!

The fabric of character

My Aunt Grace loved to knit. She'd often spend all year long laboring to make a sweater or a scarf for someone in the family. It was her way of expressing her love to us all. Practically everyone in my family had one and most of them wore their gift with pride. But, unfortunately, as my turn for one of her works of art came about, Aunt Grace had been getting on in years. Her eyesight had started to fail, her hands were deformed with arthritis and her memory was slipping, but she was bound and determined to provide everyone in our family one of her "legacies" to help "knit" our family together. One Christmas when I was 12 years old, it was my turn to receive one of her masterpieces. The sweater she knitted that year for me was a labor of love but, unfortunately, being the pre-pubescent ingrate that I was, I saw it as just another gift to open at Christmas and a disappointing one at that. It was the wrong style, the wrong size, the wrong shape - one arm was a little longer than the other, the stripes were crooked and the color was not cool, at least according to my preteen standards. However, under my shell of trying to be the tough, cool teenager I had hoped to be, I felt an inkling of appreciation for her efforts and the demonstration of her love. However, only through prompting from her sister, my mother, would I force myself to wear it, but only when she said so. Other than those times, it sat folded in my dresser drawer waiting to be exhibited, hopefully for Aunt Grace's eyes only, or for me to outgrow it. I really didn't want to hurt her feelings, but I also didn't want to have to endure the wrath of my mother. For both reasons, I wore it anyway even though I didn't like it. It wasn't until I matured into an adult that I could understand the worth of Aunt Grace's gift.

When I was diagnosed with multiple sclerosis, thinking of it as a gift was furthest from my mind. Even now, one might think it odd for me to say that having MS is a "gift," especially in light of my hatred for it, but for me to say or think otherwise would only underrate the positive influence it has had on my life. To think of it as anything other than a gift only justifies all the negative aspects of this debilitating disease.

In reality, this offering of MS as a part of my life is not the true gift, but, rather, how I respond to it. Not unlike the sweater from my Aunt Grace, my response to how I "wear" my MS is what makes it a gift. It is also not unlike the gift of life; I didn't ask for either but they are mine, to do the best I can with the conflicts and accomplishments that each brings my way.

Collaborating my careers

When my symptoms began to surface during the beginnings of my physical therapy career at Mayo, little did I know I had started a second "career" as a person with multiple sclerosis. As these symptoms gradually progressed and I realized the potential for being diagnosed with multiple sclerosis, I started a third "career" as a volunteer with the MS Society. As years passed, I recognized that these three careers were on somewhat parallel pathways, each with its own periods of growth and plateaus, doubts and rewards. Recently, when I acknowledged that they were traveling toward the same juncture, I realized my having MS was a gift. Like my Aunt Grace's sweater, I kept my MS hidden at first because I thought of it as a burden that I had to bear alone. But, when I realized others could benefit from my experiences with these three careers I began to think positively.

83

Everyone faces adversity from time to time throughout life, yet we don't normally think of it as a gift; it took courage for me to see through the haze that blinded me of this concept. It took courage for me to admit to myself that having an inadequacy or an infirmity is a gift. It took courage for me to struggle to survive the progression of my illness and the ramifications of my circumstance, and then to start telling my story. It wasn't heroic courage like a firefighter or a soldier might display. Instead, it was more of a quiet courage that I believe everyone possesses. It took that quiet courage for me to tell my story over and over again, even though others didn't want to hear it. Telling my story was cleansing, it helped me to put into perspective what was happening to me. But, it took more courage for me to keep telling my story over and over until I found something good in it! When this gift was revealed to me, I used quiet, common courage to force my story to life by using my experiences with the illness in positive ways.

However, it wasn't until later on in my journey with MS that I realized the story about my adversity is just that, a story! It took the same quiet, common courage to accept the fact that the story was meaningless; not the events themselves, but the story that enveloped them. Adversity has meaning and substance, but for me to learn from it I had to put into perspective the meaning and the magnitude of the circumstances of these trials of life. The events I experienced were real, but the story of those events was a perception. In an unconscious attempt to legitimize having MS, I told my story over and over in my head and in my conversation with others. With repetition, the exaggeration of how I dealt with MS subtly crept into the story. I wanted people to hear about my ordeal, while subconsciously I unintentionally interjected hints of misfortune and resiliency to elicit some emotional support from the listeners. The story became my subconscious way of trying to justify my life with MS to myself and to those around me. The result was that I proceeded to validate my adversity and confirm my ordeal by listening to my own story! Similarly, I am doing exactly the same thing in writing this book. While relating the trials and tribulations of dealing with MS to help others better understand the adversity surrounding the illness, I help validate its existence in me. But make no mistake about it; my story is still a story, which is only my perception of what really happened.

Fortunately, I don't live in my story as I once did. At one time the story became my life; telling how this happened or how that occurred. The story began to consume all aspects of my life. As I continued to interpret the events surrounding my MS and my story, it began to implode in on itself until I was unable to distinguish the actual events from my perceptions of those events! Whenever I tried to move on and make something positive out of the whole ordeal, I became fixated by the story. The story got in the way of my learning from the event; it prevented me from moving on.

Groundhog Day

Recently, as part of a self-awareness course, I told my story repeatedly to a group of listeners and realized I was stuck in some kind of subconscious void. Telling my story became cyclical; this happened to me, this is how I dealt with it and here I am today; this happened to me, this is how I dealt with it and here I am today; over and over the same story, the same result with no change or recourse other than to wait for the next event. It reminded me of the movie,

"Groundhog Day," where the main character is a newspaper reporter covering the annual event in Punxatawny, Pennsylvania, became caught in a similar whirlpool. He woke up one morning and experienced a day that was repeated exactly as the day before. The next day, the same events occurred and again the next day. He soon realized that each day was being repeated minute by minute the same way, right down to each precise moment. At first, he tried to fight the repetition. He anticipated every predetermined event and angrily confronted the participants, as if they were the cause of his dilemma. As the days continuously repeated themselves he began to focus on taking advantage of the daily replication of his life. He retained the memory of the previous day's experience and built his life around the redundancy, including the courting of a woman he met the first day. In the movie, their love breaks the spell and they get on with life as a couple in love.

For me, I realized that to get on with my life, I needed to break the spell of my never-ending, Groundhog Day-type of story with MS. I needed to abandon my story, which was the driving force in my life. The story was my life in the past tense, which was determining my life in the present tense. When I stopped using my story to determine what my present life was, I began to use my future as the impetus for positive change in my present life. When I put the past in the past tense and the future in the present tense, I was set free to create any future possibility I could imagine. Setting forth opportunities for the future has expanded my life with MS, rather than restricted it.

The process of changing from the past tense to the future tense and creating a possibility wasn't easy. Up until I experienced my "Groundhog Day" epiphany, I believed I was positively engaging my MS and thought I was making constructive changes in my life. But, when I became aware that my story about past events was actually impeding my ability to progress I was able to renovate my life from a reactive realm of living, into a creative one. I am now able to pursue the possibilities of future endeavors I create for myself.

The hardest part of my transformation was realizing that my story was meaningless! This was another revelation. I had to admit to myself that my traumas and sorrows, successes and triumphs were pointless if I didn't utilize them to generate a future free from the confines of my MS. I had been trying so hard to impress upon myself about surviving an ordeal of living with a chronic, progressive illness that I didn't recognize my response to MS as a significant gift. When I gave up living my story, I was able to move to a new level of being, despite any future adverse effects I may encounter from my MS. Giving up my story freed me to create the possibility in my life of being strong and inspirational!

The most dramatic change in my life occurred when I re-established a closer relationship with my children and their mother. While I had maintained a bond with my son, Grant, through the years of chaos, the relationship with my daughter, Greta, was extremely tumultuous, which was a result of her stepfather's attempt to divide us. The start of this change occurred when I approached their mother to begin a supportive friendship. Skeptical at first, she became receptive to the possibility of developing a reciprocal appreciation of our struggles with our divorces and a mutually supportive approach toward our children after the despicable behavior of their stepfather was revealed. The main focus of our renewed parental relationship was to resolve our differences and support our children during the transitions in their lives. This understanding between us slowly gained strength over time as did the trust between my children and me. The four of us are very close now!

Even though the story regarding my MS is meaningless, how I dealt with the adversity surrounding my life with MS has strong significance in providing the building blocks of my future. My wish in sharing my experiences with MS is for others to get out of them by reading, what I have learned from them by living. However, my ultimate goal is to have others reach the same level of confidence for the future that I have.

It is for these reasons, I share my gift.

Chapter Five

Struggle is Therapeutic...

The butterfly gains strength enough to fly through its struggle to free itself from the confines of the cocoon!

Learning to cope

At one time I thought having multiple sclerosis was the worst thing that could ever happen to me. I didn't know how to overcome all the destructive negative forces acting against me, which led to many tragedies in my life either as a result of the illness itself, or indirectly, as a consequence of my own self-fulfilling prophecy.

I now know that many of the best years of my life are still in store. But for me to learn how to cope with MS in positive, healthy ways, I had to plot a course through a maze of anger, remorse and physical destruction, navigating toward opportunity and success. I eventually surmised that by struggling against the MS, I was really fighting against myself and that the internal battle is as destructive as the MS itself. I have come to realize I can alter the course of my inevitable demise and direct it toward a journey of success. This wasn't an easy task by any means, and it took a long time just to realize the positive possibilities for my life. It took courage to start acting on those visions of hope and aspirations. It took even more time and courage to change these ambitions into opportunities, which I consider a lifelong endeavor.

Coping with multiple sclerosis is a challenge. I struggle year-to-year, day-to-day and sometimes moment-to-moment with its progression. It affects most aspects of my life and will consume me if I allow it to. It controls my body in many ways but I choose to embrace it, challenge it and envelop it with my being. Someone once said, "Adversity builds character," but there are times when adversity tends to destroy my spirit. Whenever I am faced with a new challenge, albeit physical, emotional, financial or spiritual, I have to emotionally readjust and physically readapt to a new level of comfort. But it is this level of comfort I seek that ultimately holds me back from making choices I need to better my situation. I used to be afraid to alter my comfort zone because I hadn't always made the right choices. It seemed as if I kept making the same mistakes over and over; much like the aforementioned "Groundhog Day" cycle. I was afraid to make a change for fear I would make a mistake again, so as a consequence, I tended to stop putting myself in positions where I had to make a decision. But for me to move forward into the future, I have to get out of my comfortable cocoon of complacency. When I think outside of this insulating bubble, I am able to make

93

decisions, whether they are right or wrong. Frequently, I learn more from the latter than I do from the former.

It is no easy task to ignore the changes in my body, discount the losses in my life and face the fear of the future. I continually search for inner strength, explore introspectively for positive resources and listen to my spirit. In fact, you might say I survive because of my illness, for it is how I cope with adversity that makes me stronger. I am not a victim of MS, nor am I mere survivor - I am a conqueror! What I have conquered is not the MS, but rather, the challenge it entails. For me to reach this point, I had to take responsibility for the things I had control of and let go of my attempt to fight the things I didn't.

I believe the struggle continues to be therapeutic. I used to practice self-defeating ways to struggle with my life and my MS, and these were barriers to my betterment. However, as I squinted through the fog of despair I began to see there are different ways to struggle. I eventually discovered and nurtured more self-protecting ways to struggle with my beast.

Managing the waves of adversity

Struggling with the barriers created by having MS in my life reminds me of a time when I was a kid learning how to swim. I grew up in northern New Jersey. While there were many lakes around where I lived, unfortunately, they were all private and not readily accessible to me. So, for me and the other boys in my neighborhood to go swimming, we had to walk or ride our bikes along a long stretch of railroad tracks to a dam that divided two of the lakes. Of course, the homeowners on the lakes weren't real pleased with a bunch of pre-adolescent boys swimming on the other side of their lake, and on their side of the tracks, as it were. But all we wanted to do was swim at the dam, far from their beaches where, ironically, my future wife was learning to swim. My friends and I didn't think we were doing anything wrong, but the homeowners did. Occasionally, some burly men would row their boats across the lake to try to chase us away. Of course we just laughed and taunted them with boyish insults. Sometimes they would call the railroad police and they would chase us away. At other times we had to battle other boys from nearby homes who didn't want us there either. Despite those barriers - busy railroad tracks, irate landowners, railroad cops and rival kids – we somehow managed to get enough time in the water to learn the basics of swimming.

I had similar hindrances learning to cope during the earlier years of my MS. Every time I tried to make sense out of what was happening to my body, I encountered impediments. The symptoms were subtle enough to be absent to the observer's eye, but internally I was experiencing changes that were affecting my ability to physically perform my activities of daily living. However, whenever I went to the doctors to have them sort out what was happening, I was met with negative results of tests and probes, and basically told to, "Go home and forget about it!" or in essence, "Get out of here kid, you can't swim in our lake!" I was in a twilight zone of needing an explanation regarding my symptoms and not being able to find one.

To continue with the swimming metaphor, my brothers and I were fortunate to have a father who was an avid swimmer and would often take us to the Jersey seashore during the summer to go swimming. Swimming in the ocean is quite different than swimming in a lake. Just getting into the water was a barrier of sorts, for those persistent, never-ending waves kept trying to knock me down. At first, I would turn sideways to the wave, dig my feet in the sand, lower my shoulder and wait for the impact. In most cases, I could withstand the smaller waves. But when the big one came along, I'd get knocked down no matter what I did, so sometimes I would just give into the power of the wave. My early grappling with MS was similar to my struggle with these waves; I would dig my heels in with each new encounter, but I kept getting knocked down. Sometimes I would retreat from the fight and give into the "waves" of adversities MS was sending my way. Fortunately, I came to realize that these types of responses - fighting or surrendering - were self-defeating. Both responses were negative ways of coping with problems and allowed the "waves" to win!

As I became an older, wiser and stronger swimmer, I found I could manage the ocean waves quite differently and without getting knocked over as often. I learned to bob up and down with the smaller waves and then when the big one came along, I would duck under the water and let the wave break harmlessly over my head. Granted, on occasion I would get bounced around and even knocked over, but at least I was in better control of how these waves would affect me. Similarly, I learned to bob and duck the "waves" of consequences of having MS. To do so, I vowed to become an "expert" in MS - my MS! My increased knowledge of the illness proved to be an asset, despite the conventional medical wisdom of the time, which was to resist educating patients about disease. Fortunately, the concept of "knowledge is power," is more prevalent today.

Later on, I matured into a very strong swimmer. I became even more competent in managing the ocean waves. When a big one came along, I would start swimming in the same direction, catch it, and ride it into the shore. Though body surfing was risky at times, I was in much better control of my response to the waves. As I matured with my experiences with MS, I learned that these two responses to struggling - adapting and "going-with-the-flow" - were positive means for managing the "waves" of difficulty in my life. So, as a new symptom or an exaggeration of an old one comes my way, I find ways to modify my life to accommodate the change while optimizing my potential to grow from the experience. I now manage rather than fight; cope rather than surrender.

Another metaphor of life

I also learned about struggle and adversity from my competitive athletic experiences; first as a football player, then as a coach. There are many parallels in the game of football and the game of life. They both involve training, competition, teamwork, decision-making, and wins and losses as a result of those decisions. The greatest lesson I learned from both is taking personal responsibility for my role in the game. The other coaches and I tried to instill in our players the positive ideals and values we learned from our coaches. We were hopeful those ideals would carry over into their lives, as they did into ours. The clichés we used on our players are still fresh in my mind:

"When the going gets tough, the tough get going!"

"Winners never quit and quitters never win!"

"It's not the size of the dog in the fight; it's the size of the fight in the dog!" - My all-time favorite.

These may sound corny, but even today they help me put my struggles with MS into perspective.

Recently, I was reminded of these values

when I went back to the New Jersey high school where I taught and visited with the men I coached with all those years ago. They too had experienced trials and tribulations in their lives. As we told our stories, we all related our football days to our "games of life." The values we had learned as players and preached as coaches had carried us through some pretty tough times. Tales of death, divorce and disease were highly emotional. How some of us had survived our struggles in life was extraordinary. But with all the rhetoric, we agreed on one thing: applying the lessons we learned in football to our lives wasn't as easy as quoting a few sayings. In our attempts to overcome our struggles, we all stuck to the conviction of playing on in the face of adversity. We all ran into some formidable barriers that we had to overcome before we could learn the lessons of the struggles and apply them positively in our lives.

Ocean waves and football games are nothing compared to the adversities brought on by having a chronic illness, but the lessons learned from these experiences help me to find ways to coexist with the disease and maintain a positive approach to life. The illness is what it is; I am whoever I create myself to be. It takes creativity to envision the possibilities I want for myself and the persistent courage to make them realities.

An awakening

But, it also took a sea of change in how I view my existence. As I looked at the value of coping with these challenges brought on by the disease, I was awakened to the reality that the problem was not with the disease, but how I viewed myself with the disease and how I reacted to those perceptions. When I was diagnosed with MS I believed I would be severely disabled and in a nursing home within in a matter of a few years. I projected myself into the worst-case scenario because of my experiences with patients with MS during my medical education. As my MS has slowly progressed over the 26 years after my diagnosis, I have come to realize that it would be a very long time before MS incapacitates me beyond when I could take care of myself. In many respects, MS is an encumbrance that is tolerable at best. MS is physically restricting, but I have been able to accommodate with the use of a wheelchair, walkers and other assistive aides. While these devices expand my physical capabilities, it is the emotional adaptation to the changes in my body that is the most restricting. Previously, when I viewed myself as being physically incompetent, I narrowed my emotional capacity. I reacted to my limitations with all the physical accommodations I needed, but I relied on them to be the basis of my adaptation to the disease process. Even though I had made many adaptations to the emotional consequences of having MS - divorce, family turmoil and career changes - I made only subtle attempts at maintaining my healthy self. I knew how to exercise, eat well and maintain my health, and I had made attempts to improve myself physically but I wasn't practicing what I preached. In an attempt to fight the illness, I gave of myself through volunteering to help me feel better about my own situation. I was helping others by providing therapy, but I was really fighting against my own situation and losing. Even though I had all the concepts of a positive struggle - adapting, accommodating and acclimating – I wasn't utilizing my skills of swimming in the vast "ocean of adversity" or my football game philosophy in my "game of life."

When I ended up in the hospital with the flu in 2000, I realized I had to practice what I preach and change my game plan. The incident was a very humbling experience. Actually, it was humiliating! I hadn't taken care of myself and I found myself in front of my peers with whom I had worked with in the past, but now I was the patient. Other than after my spine surgery, I hadn't been seen by a physical therapist as a patient with MS. I was treating myself, but to paraphrase an old saying, "A physical therapist that treats himself has a fool for a patient." Though the experience of being hospitalized frightened me, it also helped me to appreciate a potential I hadn't considered. When I asked myself, "If something like this were to occur again, how prepared would I be to prevent being hospitalized?" Unfortunately, I had to admit, "I am ill-prepared!" The accessibility of my home was mediocre, as were my attempts at fitness; I hadn't taken care of my physical needs. I needed to start now to prepare myself for the future. Before I got home, I accepted the challenge of confronting this wave of adversity by bettering my environment and myself!

Patterns, perceptions and potentials

For me to accomplish any future goal, I had

103

to change my perception of who I am and my view of other people's perception of me. I have a perception of who I am based on my experiences with MS and my personality. How I have dealt with my successes and failures with MS is the fundamental fiber of my existence. How I weave that fiber becomes the cloth of my character and how I perceive myself wearing this cloth defines who I am in my mind's eye. But, I had been weaving a cloth that was a reaction to my MS. Each time my physical abilities changed, I redefined who I was in respect to what I lost. I now redefine who I am based on the perception of who I want to be. This profound change in my viewpoint is the inspiration for this book. It has become the frame of mind for my existence.

The pattern of that "character cloth" changes as more fibers of success and failure are introduced into the design. The new design changes the perception of who I am. I may not be able to change the fibers, but I can change the design of the weave through power of will and the power of won't. My "will" is to reconstruct and redefine my "self" as my body changes with the erosion of my function. My "won't" is to not give into the emotional degradation brought on by my reaction to MS. These two concepts need to be nurtured through encouragement and support; two things I didn't always have. When these aren't present, I rely on my own internal fortitude to pursue my goals.

At one time I thought of myself as a failure both as a husband and father because I didn't make decisions that were for the benefit of my family. I was so engrossed in my MS I didn't see the erosion of my relationships with my wife and my children. MS had consumed my everyday thoughts with fears of situations I thought were going to happen: disability, loss of employment, financial hardship and dependency. I viewed myself as the person I thought I would become. My self-identity was at an all-time low when I got divorced, had surgery, changed jobs and developed new symptoms. These events were as a result of my MS, directly or indirectly, but how I reacted to these life changes was based on how I thought others might view me as a person with MS. I was so influenced by how someone might judge me because of my MS, I judged myself negatively. When I realized my opinion of myself was based solely on how I thought someone else might think of me, I also realized how ineffective I was. I was paralyzed by my views of the perceptions of others.

I now view my life as if it was an athletic event and my body is the venue within which I play. However, despite what one may think, MS is not my opponent! I cannot defeat the MS itself, but I am able to combat my negative reactions to the decay it imposes within. My opponent, in essence, is my response to the disease, not the disease itself. Not unlike with any competition, when I think my opponent will beat me, I will lose. As I create the possibilities of winning, even against insurmountable odds, I improve the potential for winning. In any rivalry, I tend to compete with more zeal when the opponent is strong. When the opponent is weak, the challenge is reduced and the competition loses its appeal. I am at my best when the opponent is challenging me. With MS, when things are stable, the challenge is reduced and the demand to struggle is lessened. I then tend to fall once again into that comfortable cocoon of complacency, which is so non-competitive. As I begin to feel too much contentment with where I am at the time, I rely on my concepts of the therapeutic value of the struggle. Every conflict needs a goal to achieve, a means with which to confront the opponent and an action plan to achieve victory. My struggle is a life-long endeavor against the devastating effects of MS. My goal is to be in the best physical, mental and emotional condition as possible to be prepared for the time when the cure and reversal of its symptoms are available. My game plan is to learn from the battles I experience and continue to redefine my engagement strategies with my foe, which is undoubtedly an ongoing process.

My MS will progress, I will get older, I will become more disabled and I will die, these are givens. Until that final Day of Judgment, I won't give up pursuing my fundamental goal, to be healed and free from the shackles of MS. The way I continue on my quest is to believe in myself, practice what I preach and manage the forces over which I have some control.

Chapter Six

Anger and Depression

Anger and depression are neither the problem nor the solution; what I do with each of them is.

Slippery slopes

There were many times throughout my "career" with multiple sclerosis when I was frozen with fear and depression. I often felt as if I had slipped into a wide abyss of rejection; falling down into a dark, bottomless pit of despair where I couldn't get out. The slopes were slippery and steep, and the harder I tried to ascend those slopes, the deeper into the abyss I fell. At times I felt my only solution, my only way out was, as Shakespeare once asked, "Oh death, where is thy sting?" However, I thank God I didn't act on those feelings. There were times where I could see flickers of hope that brightened into the light at the end of the tunnel, though I prayed that it wasn't the proverbial train instead. During those periods of remorse and resolve, I realized I needed to do something to better my position in life. I knew I had to stop having a pity party, for I was the only one invited and it wasn't any fun. With God's help, I knew I had to stop feeling sorry for myself. I had to stop beating myself up over the unrealistic guilt I was feeling for having MS and seemingly failing as a father and husband. As I eventually discovered, the MS wasn't the cause of my anguish; it was my response to it. I had to stop being angry with my ex-wives, my kids and myself. I had to direct my anger toward the MS and away from myself.

I had been so focused on my inabilities and my losses that I lost sight of my abilities - what I still could do and what I might be capable of doing. I was so blinded by the misdirected anger that I couldn't see the possible good in all that was going on around me. I was so focused on the negatives that I didn't see the positives to my life with MS, though they were staring me in the face.

I didn't see the relationship at first, but my depression and anger are interdependent. There are times when I'm so angry with my MS, I could scream! Everyday when I get out of bed, I'm reminded of the hindrances it causes in my life. With each movement I try to make, I'm reminded of the physical damage MS has done to my once-athletic body. As I slowly put one crutch forward, then one foot, then another crutch and so on, I am reminded of the precarious position in which I have been placed. As I push my wheelchair through the mall or grocery store, I'm reminded of the adjustments to my physical limitations I have had to make. My body and the equipment I use to adapt to my limitations continually remind me of the war that is being waged within; of the battles I have won and lost; and of the conflicts yet to be encountered. It is all of these and more that motivate me; and anger is the main driving force.

Even though I'm entrenched in a war against the effects of MS, I'm winning the battles against remorse, sorrow, depression and anger. Though I have feelings of resentment and disdain toward my plight, I am prompted to count my blessings, for my MS is temperate in nature compared to many. But my gratefulness for what I do have doesn't dissuade me from battling to improve my state of affairs. I continue to labor toward the betterment of my situation. I try not to dwell on what I've lost but rely on my accumulated anger to motivate me to persevere against the destruction of my body.

Knowledge is power, but anger is my switch to unleash that power.

Anger is the propulsion that drives me to try to stay ahead of the decline in my function.

Anger is the catalyst that gets me out of bed at 4:30 in the morning to go to the gym to workout before I encounter the day.

Anger fuels the fire in my belly to keep me hanging on to the abilities I have.

Anger is the channel through which I fight to regain what I have lost through benign neglect.

Anger gives me the energy to physically, emotionally and mentally prepare myself for the time when I will be free of the confines of my torment.

Anger is the force that compels me to volunteer at the MS Society to help others with multiple sclerosis.

Anger is the stimulus to help raise the money to help find the cure and reversal of this damn disease.

Anger used to scare me, probably because I thought it was destructive. I thought I was supposed to avoid and hide it. As I was growing up, I learned how not to show my emotions and to keep them under control. I remember my mother often saying, "Don't be mad, don't be sad," as if it was wrong to feel and show those emotions. I didn't know what to do. When I did get angry, I was encouraged to suppress it. When I did communicate my anger, I felt as though I exposed a weakness, so I also developed a fear of showing my vulnerability. I learned to bite my lip when I was confronted and gaze poker-faced as if unaffected - the macho stare that invited a dare. I would look intently at my antagonist trying not to blink or look as if I wanted to back down. I was angry inside but insecure with my ability to manage the encounter. I held in my anger to avoid the conflict that I didn't think I could physically or verbally resolve. I hadn't learned how to deal with situations that required action. Rather, I found resolution with hiding behind a stoic stare. Unfortunately, that behavior never got to the bottom of problem. It only covered up the anger.

Venting anger

I eventually discovered I was able to hide my vulnerability and simultaneously dissipate some of my anger through humor. I found I could get away with avoiding angry confrontation with a quick quip or two. I made jokes and demeaned myself to transfer the anger towards the other person or situation back at me through self-ridicule. For the most part, it was an effective method at dismissing the antagonism I had at the moment. In high school, I was voted the "Class Cut-Up" because I always had the clever remark, the whimsical retort, the corny pun. Little did others know that it was a way to hide my low self-esteem and the underlying anger I held as a teenager. My humor continues to be a safety mechanism for covering up some of my anger. As an example, when I was divorced for the second time, while I was very angry for all that went on that year, I actually found myself in a better financial state. As a result I was able to buy a new car and decided to get vanity plates that read, "M S SUX." How it passed the vanity plate inspectors is beyond me; they must have been phonetically challenged! When I mentioned this to the psychotherapist I was seeing, she said, "You have a lot of rage, don't you?" Of course, I did and the license plate was a way of showing it!

My ability to hide behind a stoic stare or be humorous rather than confrontational worked fairly well during my life as a child and preteen; that is until I discovered athletics in my early teens. The act of looking macho or joking around didn't work on the football field. Athletic competition is confrontation with rules; it is controlled violence, especially in the game of football. I had to learn to vent my anger toward my opponent within the parameters outlined in the rules and with my body instead of my mouth. When I got knocked down on the football field, I had to pick myself up and challenge the guy on the other side of the line to try to do that again; there's no hiding behind a steely gaze and a joke, just "mano a mano" confrontation and resolve. Of course, from time to time, my anger would extend beyond the confines of the rules and result in a penalty.

As a teenager, I found athletics and the expression of my physical prowess to be ways that helped elevate the regard I had for the self I saw within. Sports became a way for me to vent my anger and express some of the positives I saw in myself. It also drew me away from the unruly and antisocial behavior that some of my so-called friends exhibited as they took to the streets to vent their anger. They tried to get me to join in, but I opted to vent my anger through sports when I went out for football for the first time. Athletics helped to save me from the pre-teen peer pressures that led to the inevitable criminal career that some of them pursued.

Eventually, I was able to transform my participation in football and other sports in high school and college into a fledgling career as a physical education teacher and coach. The use of my physical capabilities and interest in coaching others to improve themselves helped to again strengthen my opinion of myself, as athletics had done for me during my teenage years. However, after a short five-year stint, I became disillusioned with the teaching profession. I decided to pursue a career as a physical therapist. Teaching patients to restore their physical function through my therapeutic intervention filled the gap between my physical competencies and my emotional need to please.

I've always been a pleaser, an appeaser, a peacemaker; I normally don't like confrontation. Yet, I loved the athletic encounter, even the violent clash of bodies on the football field. I enjoy the challenge of competition. The thrill of victory and the agony of defeat that I learned through athletics have become metaphors for the learning experiences in my life. I tried to instill these concepts of learning from each encounter, win or lose, with the players I coached many years ago, and with the patients I treated as a physical therapist.

Unfortunately, off the field and out of the physical arena, I continued to practice the old ways of hiding my anger and avoiding conflict. So, when MS came on the scene and everything in my life changed, I still didn't have the resources to deal with the losses. As MS insidiously crept into my existence it began to corrode my bodily functions along with my self-identity. At first, I was stoic in my response, mostly in denial of the seriousness of my situation. I became frustrated with the glacier-like erosion of the very substance of my esteem – my physical abilities. Annoyance led to aggravation, which led to exasperation and then to all-out anger. I had no healthy way of expressing it and no one with whom I could articulate what I was really feeling. I was so good at hiding my anger that when I had opportunities to talk about it, I couldn't find the right words to express how I was feeling inside. Instead, I would bite my lip and stare poker-faced or make light of the situation with a humorous comment, as I had learned to do when I was younger. Of course, the anger didn't go away, it simmered and smoldered during my attempt to appease the sleeping monster through benign neglect, but it continued to mature and eventually grew into rage. As the intensity built I continued to cram it into my subconscious where I seemed to be able to control it. Those behaviors were neither healthy nor productive.

Anger turned inward

I needed to find outlets to physically and

117

verbally vent my growing fury, but I thought I had none. Those around me, especially my wife and children, must have thought I was handling the situation well because I could look so calm and collected on the outside. Occasionally, I would blow up inappropriately, which confused them. Consequently, they must have thought *they* were the cause of my anger, when in reality it was the MS. On the inside, I was fuming; I hated my situation. I hated what MS was doing to my body, my marriage and my life. However, I stifled my anger. I withheld my anger because of fear. I didn't want to appear defective for fear of rejection. Who would want to be with someone with MS that showed anger all the time? I held back my emotions from those around me for fear of driving them away. Ironically, one of the reasons my wife divorced me was because I didn't share my feelings with her.

When she left, I became angrier, and by burying my rage into my subconscious I became depressed. I spent many hours in psychotherapy exploring my anger and sorrow, and my response to each. I eventually learned that anger is a normal, healthy, human emotion and that it doesn't have to be justified. I came to realize that anger is a feeling that I own and therefore

I am responsible for how I deal with it. I found that anger doesn't always make sense and when I don't deal with it constructively, it causes a lot of stress, depression and destruction. Anger had become very destructive for my family and me. Eventually, I was able to explore the sources of my anger. Much of it resulted from my perceived loss of function, family and future. I hadn't completely grieved these losses and because I was so successful in withholding my anger, it became a source of my depression.

I was also pissed at the medical system of which I was ironically a part. I worked for the Mayo Clinic, the world-recognized medical center, which was renowned for diagnosing difficult-to-identify maladies, yet it took my physicians eight long, frustrating years to diagnose my MS. My antagonism towards the "system" was, of course, unrealistic. Because of the complexity of the disease and limited tests at that time, it was very difficult to support the diagnosis of almost anyone's MS. Diagnosing my MS was especially difficult because of my vague waxing and waning symptoms and their slow progression. I now know of the frustration my physicians had in trying to sort out the complexity of my symptoms. But the frustration, anger and dislike towards the

119

process have left a bitter taste of resentment towards my disease and the system within which I work. I don't hate the sinner, just the sin, as it were. Sometimes the system was unkind, but the end result, multiple sclerosis, was most unkind.

After my diagnosis there was relief that soon turned to grief. The whole process of acquiring a loss, grieving that loss, developing a new loss and then grieving that new loss has compounded the overall grief of having MS! The complexity of mixing the phases of grief, particularly the overlapping of anger and depression, made it extremely difficult to differentiate between the reality of the disease and my disabilities, and the perception of life and my abilities. The losses are unpredictably repeated over and over as the illness progresses. They are variable and inevitable, which makes the future unpredictable, yet not surprising. These all contribute to a level of incomplete grieving and contribute to a chronic state of sorrow.

The anger at my ex-wife, the medical field and my MS was detrimental to me. It caused me to demean the person who I thought I was and the person I presumed I would become. I feared the future and potential loss of function, which only promoted my self-destruction. I was executing my own self-fulfilling prophecy of disability; I was becoming the way I thought I was supposed to be or at least the way the "system" was insinuating I would be.

The anger-depression connection

I eventually came to realize that when I was depressed, I wasn't angry. The depression seemed to deaden my anger. Depression was a sedative that dulled my anger, my senses and my drive to move on. The depression was also the precursor to the apathy I felt toward doing anything positive about my situation. This downward spiral tended to creep into my life because I didn't deal with my anger.

I also noticed that when I was aware of my anger, I was less depressed and less apathetic. Anger has now become my way of getting out of my emotional slump. When my anger is directed away from the things I've lost and more toward my resurrection, I become more positive about my outlook on life. There seems to be a fine line between my destructive depression and my activating anger. When I let my circumstances fester negatively, I become more depressed. When I recognize the constructive aspects of my circumstance, I get angry with myself for letting my self-esteem slide toward the abyss of depression. But, then again, I need to reach that brink so I am better able to pull myself away from the edge and start again to work on those positives, which I can identify. Ironically, the depression becomes the trigger to excite my anger, which becomes the impetus for affirmative encounters with my MS.

Anger is neither the problem nor the solution; depression is neither the problem nor the solution. However, what I do or don't do with both becomes either the problem or the solution; the choice is mine. I choose to channel my anger triggered by depression into positive outcomes, rather than have my anger festering into depression become the means for my self-destructive apathy. My past efforts to volunteer, do fundraising and reach out to others are a result of this anger-triggered-by-depression phenomenon. I have found that when I channel the anger against the disease rather than at my condition, I feel better about the situation and dwell on the benefits in having this disease, multiple sclerosis. The better I feel about my situation, the better I feel about who I am. This process helps me redefine who I am.

Chapter Seven

Self-Identity

Who I am is ultimately determined by who I think I can be!

The pillars of self-identity

An anonymous author once wrote, "Life is not about finding yourself, life is about creating yourself." Who I am is forged by my experiences with the many aspects of life events. Of course, a major influence regarding the continued reinventing of my identity revolves around my MS. The identity I create for the "self" that exists inside me revolves primarily around how I perceive and express myself as a man and my ability to accomplish future ambitions.

Multiple sclerosis has had a profound effect on my self-identity, inflicting deep physical, mental and emotional wounds. It has battered my self-worth bringing confusion to my perception of who I am as a man, husband, father and sexual being. As the chronicity of my illness slowly broke down my physical prowess, it continually changed how I viewed and expressed myself as the person who I originally thought I was; an athletic, healthy and somewhat self-assured male. As the illness progressed, I was confronted with the ongoing process of redefining the person I perceived myself to be. When I had difficulty getting an erection, I regarded myself as a tarnished sexual being and my overall perception of my "self," plummeted.

Impotence fed into my perception of the decline within my body and compounded the overall effect of all the other symptoms I was experiencing. The changes in my ability to walk and run were also an affront to my masculinity and my self-esteem. The problems I had with my bladder only added to the further decline in my identity.

My sexual function, sexuality and self-esteem were so intertwined in defining who I was, it was often difficult to separate them into their own unique qualities. While MS was becoming a predominate factor in my life, the delineation between the three became even more convoluted. To make any sense of my dilemma I had to ask myself, "Why is it important to separate these three entities when they are so entangled?" I eventually found the answer to be that the inherent distinctiveness of each contributes to the overall collective nature of being human in defining my identity. Although these three pillars of self-identity normally co-exist interdependently, it was possible to delineate and define each individually. This became important because when one of the three broke down, it produced a domino effect, of sorts, causing the others to wither and wilt.

When MS caused sexual dysfunction, my sexuality and self-esteem petered out as well, pardon the pun. My self-defined identity of being a healthy, athletic father and husband was deteriorating. But I eventually realized that didn't have to happen if each component was individualized and enhanced without the influence of the other. When I was able to remove the cause and effect of each and make changes in my attitude towards them individually, I was able to collectively enhance my overall perception of who I was. Although MS tried to limit who I was, it was also the MS that forced me to re-define and create the person I wanted to be within the confines of my limitations.

Sexual function and self-identity

Sex is a normal drive to satisfy a natural, inherent hunger I have, as it is with most others. As a pre-teenager I sought satisfaction through any physical contact with members of the opposite sex. Later, as a teen and young adult, it was ultimately fulfilled through intercourse. As a husband, I thought of it as a normal human expression of intimacy and eventually as an act of procreation. Although less physically satisfying, my sexual drive was fulfilled through emotional contact such as sharing desires or caring for my wife's sexual needs. I consider sex an expression of love and intimacy, the giving of one's self to another or receiving satisfaction from the other person.

As my MS progressed, my internal sexual hunger became progressively muted by my poor perception of my sexual abilities. Failure to obtain an erection propagated my fear of failure and the inability to satisfy my wife, which only reinforced my inability to get an erection. This cycle of failure and fear of failure was becoming more than just an occasional episode in our bedroom. It soon became a simile for other decreases in my physical abilities. As my walking continued to deteriorate, I became more fearful of my future ability to walk. As I lost the confidence in my physical abilities, I stopped trying to improve them. The less I did, the less I could do. I started using the wheelchair more and more, which led to a decline in my walking. As my walking declined, I became less confident in my overall abilities, which fed into my sexual dysfunction.

Adding insult to injury

When I first started to have sexual difficulties it was a major affront to my "manhood." My ability to "perform" was inhibited, despite the reassurance from a procedure called the nocturnal penile tumescence that I was physically able to get an erection. This test measures the number of erections I had while I slept. Electrodes were attached to my penis and a recorder. It was like having an electrocardiogram only it measured my erections rather than my heartbeats. When my physician told me the results, I was shocked! I had the same number of nocturnal erections of most men my age. Despite the test, I was experiencing failure and I was sure it was a direct result of my MS. Knowing my MS would most likely worsen, I thought so would my sexual failures. My wife, on the other hand, thought my inability to be aroused was a result of her not being attractive enough for me, which was not the case. But the combination of our perceptions of my ability to get an erection when I needed to had a devastating effect on our relationship.

Prior to MS, my sexual desires were stimulated through the normal psychogenic arousal pathways that started as a thought through visual, perceptual and conscious stimulation. The nerves in the spinal cord from the mid-spine control the physical responses of this psychological arousal. But as MS slowly crept into my body, these nerves seemed to be affected. My thoughts about sex seemed to be blunted. The major part of that loss of libido was probably due to my failures and fears of failure, but there also seemed to be some organic cause for my dysfunction.

The reflexogenic arousal pathways in my spinal cord also seemed to be blunted. These control the neurological responses to physical stimulation, which are initiated by the touching of the genital areas or other erogenous areas of my body. Not unlike my diminished internal hunger and psychogenic responses, my reflexogenic responses were also slowly deteriorating. My genital area was becoming less sensitive and was at times numb. There were times when I had an erection and didn't even know it until I stood up and looked down. At times I wasn't able to feel any physical stimulation, which only reinforced my lowered libido. I couldn't "get it up" when I wanted to and when I did get it up, I couldn't feel it!

Other contributing factors

The waxing and waning of the MS symptoms wreaked havoc with the physical and emotional aspects of my sexual function. Fatigue contributed to my diminished "sexual energy." Being drained of physical, emotional and mental energy, plus being in "fatigue debt" often put a damper on my sexual appetite. Fatigue also lessened my actual ability to endure the sexual act, no less the enjoyment of the process. The idea of spontaneous sexual encounters was dampened because I had to rest to have enough energy beforehand to engage in the physical activity of the moment.

The stiffness in my legs interfered with my ability to get into certain positions customarily assumed with sexual activity. They were more stiff in the prone position, so I had to change from being in the more traditional role of being the aggressor and being "on top," to one of being on the bottom and being in less control. This was difficult at first because it subconsciously wounded my male pride, however I was eventually able to look past that barrier and be aggressively submissive, so to speak.

Other symptoms of my MS also interfered with my sexual performance and enjoyment. My bladder problems became a huge disincentive for sexual activity. Who would want to be physically intimate and make love with someone who may be incontinent or smells of urine? I became overly aware of the possibility of having an accident before, during or after making love. Those concerns also heightened my fears of being incapable of having an erection; fear begets failure, which begets fear of failure.

Accommodations

On the contrary, even though spontaneous sexual activity tended to be inhibited, it became possible to use various adaptations to help overcome the obstacles that MS symptoms might cause. Negative influences would normally diminish sexual function, but in some cases, when one area of the body has diminished sensation, other areas have increased sensitivity and even hypersensitivity. Exploring these areas became exciting in itself, while the actual stimulating of these areas has become a reasonable substitute for the original.

Various medications related to male impotence, such as Viagra; alternatives to traditional positioning; and unconventional options to vaginal sex have also helped me to have meaningful sexual relations. To compensate for all the obstacles that MS threw at me, it took a lot of understanding, communication and preplanning – but I found it can be done!

Sexuality and self-identity

If sex is the inherent drive for pleasure and procreation, then my sexuality is the outward expression of my inward ability to meet those needs in myself. This involves my interaction with members of the opposite gender and the way I am able to relate toward other members of the same gender. My sexuality is how I exhibit my masculinity. I express my sexuality through how I dress, the way I speak, the car I drive, how I perform in athletic endeavors and even in how I have my hair cut. I express my sexuality in my own unique way, as do we all. My sexuality took major hits from my MS. My perception of being a coordinated, athletic, potent husband and father was being replaced by a perception of being an uncoordinated, impotent gimp. Walking tall and assertively was another way I expressed my sexuality. As my walking deteriorated, my masculinity also depreciated.

In my role as a father, the ability to "run and play" with my young children was impaired by the MS. I also thought of my divorce as showing I had failed not only as a husband, but also as a father. Although I didn't want the divorce, my participation in the marriage, or lack thereof, was a direct reflection of my ability as a husband and a father to keep the family healthy and vibrant. Fortunately, at the time, my kids were supportive of my newfound singleness and reveled in my renewed sports participation. They were able to look past my MS and my physical gracelessness when I was vertical and felt comfortable around me when I used my wheelchair. They seemed to look past my disability and love me for what I really was to them - their father. I was engaging in fatherly activities in spite of the divorce, but that seemed to falter as the divorce aged; they were becoming older and wanting more freedoms, their mother remarried, as did I, and my MS worsened. We became more separated, partly due to my lack of confidence in my being a father and partly due to other divorce dynamics.

All in all, my world was becoming one of physical, emotional and mental chaos and turmoil. My sexual dysfunction, increasing physical limitations, reduction in my role as a father, and my need to use crutches, canes and a wheelchair to aid my mobility all had an effect on how I viewed and expressed myself as a man.

Self-esteem and self-identity

If my sexuality is the way I express my masculinity towards others, then part of my self-esteem is my perception of that expression. My self-esteem involves body image, confidence in my sexuality, employment/financial status, my role in my family and even my role in society. There is also a reverse relationship in that when I don't feel good about myself, I lessen my perception of my sexuality, which in turn affects my sexual ability. This servomechanism is devastating! The physical temperament of the illness disrupts the emotional interface between the disease and my psyche.

When my wife divorced me, my fears of sexual incompetence were further compounded: "How could another woman possibly be attracted to an impotent man with MS," I wondered. This question permeated my subconscious and often spilled over to my conscious thought. Although I was able-bodied, relatively speaking - I could walk, although with a slight stagger; I was working full-time; and I exercised routinely - I still considered myself less of a man and unworthy of being in a sexual relationship; "A 40-year-old, impotent gimp is not the most attractive stallion in the herd!"

My mind was working in puzzling ways. I was trying to differentiate between my situational dysfunction and my organic dysfunction, which was very difficult. The emotional chaos of the divorce and the breakup of my family, combined with the pressure at work, trying to deal with my physical limits, mental competence and emotional stability was tenuous at times. I often had difficulty sleeping because of the mental and emotional turmoil, all of which had a profound effect on my physical endurance. This turmoil was destructive to my sexual function, sexuality and self-esteem.

I was slowly becoming less self-reliant. I was foretelling my own loss of dignity - my inability to work, diminished financial stability, loss of driving privileges and needing help with activities of daily living. I was creating the demise of my own future; MS wasn't, I was! I was becoming what I feared I would become! I was again, grieving the past, denying the present and fearing the future.

Testing the waters

Fortunately, I was able to test my sexual limits within several relationships with women who were less concerned with my "sexual abilities" and more concerned with having a caring and mutually-trusting relationship. I found that there were ways to express sexual desires other than having an erection and there were other ways to be mutually satisfying. I also began to separate my perceived lack of sexual function from my outlook towards sexuality and the manifestation of my masculine "self" all of which affected my self-esteem and self-identity.

As I separated my sexual disabilities from my physical abilities, I gained confidence in expressing my sexuality. I again explored my athletic abilities and began playing wheelchair sports – basketball, road racing and racquetball. As I gained skills in these endeavors and in my ability to handle a wheelchair, I became more confident in my mobility. When I was walking and staggering around, I felt awkward and insecure, and fatigued quickly trying to keep up with life; I

136

didn't feel very "manly." But when I was using my wheelchair, I felt smooth and confident, my mobility range increased dramatically and I had better management of my fatigue. I was also able to express my athleticism through an adaptation of my mobility and therefore was able to express my sexuality in positive ways. Coming from an athletic family and being involved with sports most of my life; my athletic ability was part of my sexuality and my self-esteem. Not being able to run around the bases, run out for a pass, or run up and down the court was a major blow to how I viewed myself as an athletic man. With wheelchair sports, I was once again fulfilling a need to express my sexuality and bolster my self-esteem.

Ironically, as I became more confident in my sexuality, I actually became more competent in my sexual function. My perception of myself and other's perception of me grew stronger. Not only was I using a wheelchair to express my sexuality through athletics, I was gracefully getting from point A to point B. I maintained my employment and function in society, all of which improved my self-esteem. I even went dancing! I felt confident in going out on a dance floor in my wheelchair and "boogying" with my vertical able-bodied peers. I learned, as Billy Joel once sang, "How to dance and still look tough!" I realized that when I felt good about myself, others felt good about me.

As I learned to manage my symptoms, many of the obstacles to having a meaningful sexual relationship were lessened and I experienced an upsurge of confidence in expressing my sexuality and self-esteem. I gained success with redefining my self-identity in positive ways.

A change of view

Going from being the supple, agile twenty-something athlete of yesteryear, to a clumsy, awkward, staggering 40-year-old, to occasionally sitting in a wheelchair and feeling good about myself was not an easy transition. Despite the positive reinforcement of using a wheelchair for athletics, mobility and social involvement, at the time I still had a dim perception of myself and believed others saw me this way as well. Sitting in a wheelchair changed my view of the world and the world's view of me. At first, I felt not only physically lower than those around me, I felt emotionally inferior. It was a self-inflicted perception, which I was eventually able to undo, but it took time, experience and a lot of positive self-talk.

Normally, when two people are interacting there is an exchange of perceptions that takes into consideration height, body type and physical ability; this usually takes place standing in front of each other. The vertical view of life is more of a mutual eye-to-eye and earlobe-to-earlobe exchange of perceptions. But, when one is sitting in a wheelchair and the other is standing, there is a distortion of perceptions. The person standing has a physically superior view of someone sitting; they look down upon the seated person with a top-of-the-head view. The "looking down upon" is not only physical, but can also be psychological. The person standing may perceive himself or herself as overlooking or over-seeing another, or as being "over" the seated person. The vertical person may not only feel superior, physically but also mentally. The person in the wheelchair may be perceived not only as being physically inept, but mentally feeble.

One example of this scenario occurred with me in real time. I entered a restaurant in my wheelchair along with the person with whom I was taking to dinner, who happened to be able-bodied. As we approached the hostess, I was wheeling myself with my eyes affixed upon hers. When we stopped, the hostess looked down at me, then immediately past me and at my friend who was standing behind me and asked, "Where would you like to sit?" I chimed in with, "*We* would like to sit in a booth." She looked down at me and then up at her and indignantly said, "Come with me." After we were seated and given menus, the server came to our table and asked my friend, "What would we like for dinner?" I never did like servers asking, what <u>we</u> wanted, as if she or he was going to join us for the meal. She didn't look at me, not even a glance acknowledging my presence. I spoke up and asked my friend what she was going to have. After my friend told me what she wanted, I gave the server her order, and then ordered my own dinner.

The whole experience with the hostess and the server was very demeaning. I felt degraded to have another individual assume I was incapable of making my own decision about where to sit or what to eat. I felt angry that the hostess and the server just assumed that since I was physically inept, I must have been mentally incompetent as well. Maybe this type of interaction was all a paranoid, self-conscious perception on my part. Maybe, the hostess and server seemed to ignore my presence because they reacted to my lack of assertiveness that they usually don't experience with men entering their restaurant. I'll never know, but I learned a lesson. How I feel about myself is reflected outward and read by others, each in their own way. For me to influence another's perception of me, I needed to change my perception of my "self." How I present myself sitting in a wheelchair is a reflection that others will sense. Of course, what they do with that sense is their responsibility. As long as I reflect positively, how they react, albeit positively or negatively, is how they are going to act in response to me. At least I learned to proactively do my part to be a positive influence in my interchange with others. Now, as I enter a situation where I need to interact with the vertical community, I take the initiative to start the conversation with others in a positive manner before the others get a chance to perceive me as being incapable of making choices for myself and the person with whom I'm having dinner.

On the lighter side, I have become very aware of my perceptions and views from the seated position. Interacting with society from the wheelchair level to the extent that I do, I see more of a "belly button and buttocks" view of life, or what I refer to as, "the world of butts and guts;" believe me it isn't all that great, except on occasion. This is especially evident with the rise of obesity and clothing styles emphasizing midriff exposure. Getting on an elevator while sitting in a wheelchair and having large guts and butts staring me in the face is not a pleasurable adventure!

Making positive moves

Before becoming a physical therapist I thought of people who used wheelchairs as being old and infirm. But as I became exposed to the medical model of life, I saw the wheelchair being used usually in dependent roles by many people with disease and injury. Someone was usually pushing the individual in the wheelchair. Maybe that was the reason for my fear of using a wheelchair; I had difficulty imagining myself as being diseased and dependent! So, it was no wonder that I was really scared to use a wheelchair, at first. However, I did get a different perception of someone using a wheelchair when I became acquainted with the recreational therapist who was paraplegic from a car accident. He was totally independent. He graduated from college, drove his own car, worked full-time, was married and had 2 children - all after he became paralyzed. He also played wheelchair basketball and racquetball, and competed in wheelchair road racing! He was personable, positive and perceptive. It wasn't until after I had talked with him did I realize that someone like me, with a walking disability, was eligible to play organized wheelchair sports. I didn't have to be "confined" to a wheelchair to play in a wheelchair. So, the first time I used a wheelchair was to play wheelchair basketball as part of a local team. I felt totally awkward the first time I got into the wheelchair. I didn't know how to move and turn as gracefully as the other team members. I was on the court with people who were injured or had debilitating conditions and had to use the wheelchair for everyday functions. I felt blessed that I was able to stand up from the chair and walk, not real well mind you, but at least I was still able to be vertical. However, the advantage disappeared when we were on the court because my wheelchair skills left a lot to be desired. Others literally wheeled circles around me. But, I quickly learned from them. I eventually learned from trial and error -

a lot of error I might say - to wheel up and down the basketball court without running into other players or falling out onto the floor. I also learned how to propel the wheelchair, dribble and pass the basketball, simultaneously and without violating the rules of the game (most of the time.) My hands took a beating because I was forever pinching my fingers between other chairs; wheelchair basketball is definitely a contact sport!

Off the court, I also learned how to "pop wheelies," jump curbs and go up and down escalators. As I gained these skills, I became more confident in being in the wheelchair, at least while I was with others who used them. Unfortunately, I feared going out in public by myself. I was still afraid of how people would view me. I didn't want to be thought of as being infirm and "confined" to a wheelchair. Even though I knew the men and women with whom I played wheelchair sports weren't that way, I feared the able-bodied, vertical world would. This was possibly because I was also part of that world when I wasn't playing wheelchair sports. I was caught between two worlds, vertical and sitting. I felt awkward in each, both physically and emotionally.

My need to use a wheelchair became more and more apparent at work when I couldn't hide my clumsiness and exhaustion. My fatigue became overwhelming and I had difficulty performing my job. So it was at work when I first used the wheelchair in public. I had forewarned my immediate supervisor, but it was impossible to express to my co-workers the reason I was using it. Although I felt like screaming at the top of my lungs, "I have MS!" I really didn't want anyone to know. I was caught in a dilemma: I had to use the wheelchair to continue with my employment, but I didn't want people to think I was physically or mentally incompetent to continue with my employment. That was the stigma of MS that I carried with me.

The first time I used the wheelchair at work my image of my "*self*" was altered even with all the skills I had learned on the basketball court. I viewed myself as less than whole; I was diseased, in poor health, infirm compared to those in the "vertical" world. It meant that I had lost physical function and I felt that I had lost the perception of the confidence that people had in my abilities. Not only was my body image being altered, but my mental and emotional competence within my mind's eye was also coming into question. The implication that having MS involved mental and emotional dysfunction was so pervasive, I was acutely aware of the possibility that MS could affect me more than "just" physically. This had a profound influence in my self-confidence and my self-identity.

Changes in self-identity

Paradoxically, the use of the wheelchair became the solution for my poor body image! When I was walking and staggering around, I felt clumsy and uncoordinated; I fatigued easily and was limited in my ability to function in society. But, when I was in my wheelchair I felt coordinated and free of confinement. I could move quickly and smoothly from point A to point B while conserving my energy. This freedom of movement negated my original fear of being confined to a wheelchair. Of course, the type of wheelchair I used made a huge difference. The typical wheelchair of the time was heavy, clunky and difficult to maneuver. The sport wheelchairs were lightweight, quick and extremely maneuverable. When I used the chair in public I became agile and confident in managing my environment. Being able to independently open doors; go up and down curbs; maneuver around people; and even go up and down escalators boosted my self-esteem. All of this combined with my athletic expression through wheelchair sports elevated my self-identity to a level above ordinary, able-bodied individuals.

I actually became condescending towards people who were not as well off as I was physically, not people with disabilities, mind you, but with able-bodied individuals who I thought were physically inferior to me if I hadn't been disabled. It was totally wrong for me to feel this way! It was a rebound from my feelings of inferiority toward myself; it was a way to enhance my self-worth at the expense of my perception of others around me. It actually reached a point to where I would purposely avoid interaction with people whom I felt may want to help me with an environmental challenge. I eventually came to realize I represented other people with disabilities. Not unlike other situations in our society, how I conduct myself as a man, father, husband, physical therapist, employee and as a person with a disability, reflects upon all others in those groups.

New philosophy

I now feel that I don't need to prove myself to anyone. The expression of my identity reflects my positive attitude toward who I perceive my "self" to be through my mind's eye. This attitude has helped to free me of the psychological confines in which had I placed myself.

Recently, I decided to expand my philosophy of struggle. I had become so comfortable using the wheelchair that I neglected to walk when I could. I would walk around my house with a wheeled walker; but seldom, if ever, would I try to walk with my walker or crutches outside of my protected emotional womb. I felt more masculine using my wheelchair in the community because my mobility was sleek and quick. When I use my walker I am slow and clumsy, so the thought of using my walker in front of people outside of my close friends and family was an affront to my masculinity, my sexuality.

I had come full circle. I had found a way of boosting my self-identity by adapting very successfully to my limitations. However, my adaptations led to a further decline in my abilities. Recently, I decided to look beyond my perceptions of my self-identity as a coordinated, mobile, athletic-acting man in a wheelchair and began to accept the struggle with my activities of daily living and work by starting to use a walker in place of using my wheelchair when I could. This has exposed me to a whole reversal of my adapted image to one of being awkward and inept. The concept of reversing my decline is built upon my philosophy of struggle.

Adding to my positive perceptions of my self-identity has been my ability to cope with the various symptoms of my MS. I have become an expert in my MS through the self-management of my fatigue, bladder dysfunction, stiffness and weakness, which has boosted confidence in my sexual function, sexuality and self-esteem redefining a positive self-identity!

Chapter Eight

Wellness

Age is the linear part of life over which I have little control. But, life is three-dimensional and it's up to me to fill in the width and depth.

Can illness and wellness be compatible?

Tucked away somewhere in the back of my mind are memories of a time when I didn't have to fight weakness and stiffness just to stand; when I didn't have to think about every step I take; and when I didn't have to struggle with fatigue to survive my day. Just recently, I was reminded of those times when I was talking to an old friend whom I hadn't seen for quite awhile. Although he knew I had MS, he didn't realize I needed to use a wheelchair to get around until he saw me. He referred both to the MS and the wheelchair then added, "I remember how active you were before you got sick!"

I considered it strange that he thought I was inactive and referred to me as being sick. Did he think those things about me just because I was sitting in a wheelchair? Does having MS mean that I'm sick? I may have an illness but I certainly don't feel "sick" and just because I'm sitting in a wheelchair, doesn't mean I'm sedentary! After his remark, I thought to myself, "I am very active and feel very well, thank you, despite what you may think! In fact, I'm more active and feel better because I use a wheelchair!"

That incident stirred up resentment towards him, plus brought to mind several disturbing queries such as:

"Is it possible to have an illness and not feel ill?"

"Is it possible to be in a wheelchair and not have others think of me as being inactive and sick?"

"Is it possible to have MS and be well?"

Answering "No" to any of these questions would mean I have a problem. However, because I choose to be well and live a powerful existence, I can answer these questions with a resounding "Yes!"

The concept of wellness has been around for quite a while, although it doesn't seem to be practiced very often. Today, our society is overweight, inactive and overstressed. Illnesses and conditions, such as obesity, diabetes, heart disease, stroke, lung disease and some cancers are on the rise and are often a reflection of lifestyle choices and, therefore, are potentially preventable. Prevention involves getting appropriate nutrition; eating a moderately-balanced diet; avoiding tobacco, alcohol and drug consumption; learning to relax; and exercising regularly. These are the basis of the overall scheme of wellness – MS or no MS! Unfortunately, adversity, such as having a chronic, progressive illness like MS, works against the concept of wellness. Over-indulgence of food and harmful substances; coupled with too much television and computer usage; and not enough physical activity reinforce an escape from the realities of dealing with misfortune. Instead of trying to use the concepts of wellness to help overcome the situation, the tendency is to run the other way. Seeking comforts to soften the blow of trials and tribulations becomes a lifestyle. This comfort zone of misleading pleasure with rewards of instant gratification is reinforced over time. Wellness tends to be erased from the day-to-day vocabulary of life. I, like many people with MS and other chronic illnesses, tend to fall into the snare that began with being a "victim." This role then becomes more fortified through self-fulfilling prophecy.

I had to ask myself what it means to be "well." The word "well" is interesting for it has many meanings and is so overused. If I were to describe a man's wealth, I might say he was, "well off." If I were to describe a football team's accomplishments, I might say, "They played well." If I were to describe my car, I might say it was "well made" and that it "ran well." But, I wouldn't use these examples to describe my life with multiple sclerosis. Indeed, at one time I thought of myself as being quite "un-well."

Growing from adolescence into adulthood in the 1960's, I remember society as being less stressful, more physically active with exercise and recreation, and a diet less influenced by fast food and poor nutrition. Nevertheless, I also remember the concept of wellness as being some mysterious, magical, mood of the mind. It was supposed to be an experience when the mind and spirit converged as one. Of course, this would occur only when one bonded with some guru, who was sitting, playing a sitar, on the top of a mountain covered with flowers. This seemed to be the only time when one could really get in touch with one's inner self and be well. At least that's what the flower children led us to believe.

In reality, wellness is more than just a spiritual awakening within the confines of our bodies; wellness is more comprehensive than that. It involves living a healthy lifestyle, combined with a balance of physical, mental, emotional and spiritual welfare. That still may sound like "the guru on the mountain" concept, but wellness is holistic and inclusive. Wellness for me, with an adversary like MS, means physically trying to perform to the best of my ability, mentally making the most of my capability and emotionally developing stability. I also strive for spiritual peace and reduce the risk factors within my lifestyle. For complete wellness, I reach out and give to others that which I have received; my knowledge, my experience and my positive outlook.

Wellness, however, is not just a goal for me to realize, but a means by which I can achieve other goals. My primary goals are to live long enough to experience the cure and be in the best possible shape to endure the rigors of reversing the damage done by MS to my body! To reach that goal, I need to be strong and fit; be free of excess body weight; avoid preventable diseases; and be mentally sharp, emotionally stable and spiritually sound. To obtain that goal, I need to practice "wellness." But how can I do all of those things and have multiple sclerosis at the same time? I came to the realization that I've "been there, done that," and have been wearing the t-shirt with "The World Tour of Despair and Hopelessness" printed on the back. I had to remove and burn it for me to move on!

To have MS and live "well" is a lifelong endeavor. Wellness is a dynamic state of mind; a philosophy that dictates my behavior, grows with determination, swells with persistence and is rewarded with conviction. Wellness is an enduring practice of reinforcing the concepts of healthy living, managing the controllable aspects of illness and preventing future maladies. However, achieving wellness is not without barriers and obstacles.

Emotional wellness

A big barrier to my achieving wellness has been the emotional adjustment to my disease. With each loss, I had to go through various phases of grief including denial, bargaining, depression, anger, fear, remorse, regret and sorrow. It took courage to accept that these are normal, yet destructive when not addressed. However, the grief associated with my MS tended to be collective. I would grieve each new loss, while continuing to adjust to old losses. I simultaneously grieved the past, denied the present and feared the future.

This emotional process contributed to my physical fatigue and became a component of the "fatigue pie," which fed into barriers to wellness; being distraught and fatigued go hand-in-hand. People with chronic depression, as a result of mental illness, often experience fatigue causing their need to rest or sleep often. Anyone may experience fatigue with emotional upset because of the physical, mental or economic situations of life.

Emotional trauma is, of course, no stranger to someone with MS. The emotional adjustment to the day-to-day rigors of MS may cause depression and despair as a part of the grieving process. Along with the depression, there may be other emotional upsets, such as anger, guilt and fear. I have been able to deal with my MS through what I like to call, "disciplined grieving." I know I will have to grieve any loss that comes my way. I acknowledge the process and discipline myself to accept the phases of grief as they come about.

There have been many times during my multiple sclerosis experience when I have been depressed. The major periods were after I was diagnosed with MS and after each of my two divorces - when the gravity of family and economical affairs weighed heavy on my heart, my mind and my central nervous system. Not only were my nerves and muscles failing me, but I also believed those with whom I trusted to love me were abandoning me. The physical pain of my body's erosion was miniscule compared to the emotional pain of rejection, the scars of which have finally healed. Early on, as my family seemed to have deserted me, I renounced myself as useless and assumed my physical talents to be the same. I fell into a deep, dark, pit of despair and found myself, at times, frozen in depression. Periodically, I found myself unable to function physically and make even the simplest of decisions. I found it hard to concentrate and accomplish the most effortless tasks. I constantly felt physically exhausted and emotionally drained. I was lost in a desolate marsh of rejection and stuck in its emotional quicksand. It seemed as though the harder I tried to fight my way out of this quagmire, the quicker and deeper I was being pulled down. Simultaneously, the more I fought the more fatigue I experienced.

Breaking through

The major causes of my emotional barriers were related to my attempts to adjust to my predicament. A part of the emotional trauma was self-inflicted guilt, and this became a source of my withdrawal and isolation from society. This was unrealistic guilt that had no foundation. I had to learn that I didn't cause my MS, so to be guilty about something I have no control over is unrealistic. I did need to take responsibility for how I managed my disease and fatigue was a major management challenge. Often out of frustration and anger, I tended to physically over-do, which further contributed to my fatigue. And then out of fear of getting too fatigued, I would "under-do," which also contributed to my fatigue. What a dilemma! If I did too much I became fatigued; if I did too little I became fatigued. I had to learn to temper my guilt, frustration and anger to find a realistic balance of activity.

A part of the breaking through the emotional barrier was changing my perception of society's view of me as a person with MS and also as a person with a disability. Although there are laws prohibiting denial of accessibility because of a disability, there are no laws legislating attitude. My ignorance about MS and disabilities slowed my progress toward achieving my goals on the way to wellness. I needed to create the attitude that my perception is my own and recognize the greatest barriers to wellness are self-imposed.

Taking ownership

I was constantly trying to re-identify my emotional self in the face of each new symptom or life change. I struggled to find out who I was as a parent, a spouse, an employee and a person. Walls of self-pity and self-doubt, diminished self-worth and low self-esteem seemed to be formidable. To achieve emotional wellness, I first had to give up the fight to conquer my disease. I asked myself, "How do I stop a glacier?" My answer was, of course, "I can't, but I can try to get out of its way!"

I had another emotional breakthrough when I accepted ownership for my disease and learned to manage my illness using the skills I acquired through the experience of living with it. It's my disease; I own it, it's a part of me and I have some control over how I manage it. My goal is not to control the disease itself, but to control how I cope while living with it.

Once I developed this mindset, I was able to move on. On a piece of paper, I literally listed those symptoms of MS I had some manageable control over; fatigue, spasticity and weakness, as well as bowel and bladder problems. I also listed other aspects of living not directly associated with multiple sclerosis, but which have an effect on my body; the use of tobacco, alcohol, caffeine, food and exercise. After making this laundry list of things I could successfully manage myself, I started working on them. Not all at once, but a few at a time. Some of them were easy and some I continue to work on, but then again, wellness is a dynamic, ongoing process.

More breakthroughs

To gain some control over the manageable aspect of living with MS, I had to challenge what I was putting into my body by eliminating nonessential consumption of substances that may be doing harm to my body. Not being a great user of alcohol and tobacco, it was easy to eliminate those from any part of my life. However, too much caffeine and poor eating habits were tougher to overcome. It took a lot of awareness and effort, but I was eventually able to wean myself from caffeine. I don't miss the highs or lows and headaches from too much or too little coffee.

I know being overweight is not good for anyone, but especially not for someone who has a chronic illness. Lugging 25 to 50 extra pounds around contributes to fatigue, overworks weakened muscles and limits mobility. I also know that part of what I eat will eventually come out the other end - in other words, "Garbage in means garbage out!" I have control over what goes into my body and therefore, I am responsible for the end result (excuse the pun.) Good eating habits promote good bowel habits, which are also reinforced through exercise.

I also found another aspect to good eating habits deals with my old nemesis, fatigue. I became aware of two related nutritional components; the lack of good nutrition and too much of bad nutrition. When I don't eat enough foods high in complex carbohydrates and proteins, and low in fat, I lack energy, but when I eat foods high in refined starches and sugars, and fat, I feel lethargic. Through trial and error I have been able to isolate those specific foods that make me feel good and I restrict my dietary intake to them. I rely on the concept of delayed gratification to overcome the desire of the instant gratifying taste of a candy bar or donut that later on gives me a "carbohydrate hangover."

In addition, I came to realize that the temperature of the food and drinks I consume has an effect on my body temperature. Hot food and drinks cause my core temperature to rise and conversely, cool food and drinks reduce it. There is also an increase in body temperature as a result of digestion. Just the fact that I ate something, whether it was hot or cold, contributes to my body temperature through a process called the "thermogenesis of digestion." In other words, digestion produces heat and because different foods produce different amounts of heat, the type of food I eat has an influence on the amount of heat produced in this way. For example, lasagna - with lots of cheese and meat sauce - may produce more heat with digestion than a chicken breast served with vegetables, even if they're at the same temperature. Add a heavy dessert like cheesecake to my lasagna dinner and I will have a full-blown blast furnace at work in the pit of my body, cranking out calories of heat to warm my core causing even more fatigue.

Physical wellness

Through the turbulent years in my life, I

have been able to navigate through that emotional swamp and make adjustments to my losses. But I couldn't have done it alone. I received help through professional counseling and support groups, and along with the confirming ears and validating voices of many wonderful friends. But, I ultimately learned that in order for my healing to come about, I needed to rely on my own initiatives. I had to rely on internal fortitude to claim self-empowerment, self-determination and self-discipline. The major factor that helps me with maintaining a positive self-awareness is exercise. Physical fitness plays a major role in my overall wellness. I have learned to maintain a balance of being active enough to maintain my strength and endurance, yet not over exercise and get over fatigued. I am vividly aware of the pieces of the "fatigue pie," two of which are the physiologic causes of muscle and nerve fatigue associated with MS. These two reasons tend to go hand-in-hand, but are separate in their real definition.

Milo and the Bull

Muscles fatigue when they get overworked through activities of daily living or with structured exercise. Normally, muscles become stronger when exercised and fatigued appropriately, but need to rest to recover appropriately. Actually, this is the whole premise behind strengthening and conditioning exercises. Normal muscles respond to resistance and repetition by becoming stronger and more enduring, which means they must get fatigued to be maintained or improved.

The whole concept of building muscle strength is depicted in a story from Greek Mythology titled "Milo and the Bull." In ancient Greece, when Milo was just becoming a teenager, his father's cow gave birth to a male calf. Milo's father was a wise man who wanted his son to grow to be as big and strong a man as he was. So, he told his son, "Milo, every day I want you go out and pick up that newborn calf and carry him around the outside of the barn. Milo was used to doing what his father told him to do, although he was sometimes reluctant, for even then teenagers might question their father's wisdom. But Milo was respectful and never put up an argument for he was really an extraordinary youth who loved his father, so he set out to follow his father's mandate. Every day, Milo would go to the barn, as his father had instructed, pick the calf up and struggle to carry him about. At times Milo would think all the effort was too much, but he persisted. Well, as you might expect, the calf grew into a bull - big and strong - and Milo, too, grew into a hulk of a man - large and powerful.

Disease versus disuse

The message from "Milo and the Bull" is that routine, structured exercise will strengthen and condition muscles over time. However, MS is not a disease of my muscles, but of the nerves in the brain and spinal cord that direct the muscles. The disease renders parts of them ineffective. Of the muscles weakened as a direct result of the disease process, exercise cannot strengthen those portions. Even relatively small parts of the muscle that are weakened by the MS process will cause the whole muscle to fatigue more quickly. Indeed, these parts of the muscles may further weaken if they are overworked in an attempt to make them stronger. Muscles, weakened from deconditioning or disuse, have the potential of getting stronger; therefore, my goal is to strengthen them with proper amounts of exercise and rest. The biggest problem is differentiating between the muscles affected directly by the disease and those weakened by inactivity.

This has been a very frustrating situation for me. I have been weight training since high school and was in pretty good shape just prior to the beginning of my MS. Throughout my MS career, however, I have had a gradual decline in strength, especially in my legs, mostly because of my MS, some because of diminished activity, and partially because of my age. For me to try to exercise my muscles with the vigor of my youth only seems to weaken my muscles, rather than strengthen them. I have to exercise in moderation rather than with high intensity. I also have to be selective in which exercises will benefit me the most. I know which muscles are weak because of the MS and which are weak because I hadn't exercised them. I closely monitor how exercise affects my body, usually in hindsight, which of course, is always 20/20. If I'm feeling the effects today, of the exercise I did yesterday, I probably did too much yesterday! I then have to re-adjust my exercises in accordance with how they adversely affect my fatigue and overall function, which is an ongoing challenge, to say the least. The most frustrating aspect of this is that everyday is different. I can exercise at a high intensity one day without carryover fatigue, but on another day, the same exercise routine may leave me very fatigued.

The benefits of exercise are far reaching for they help me manage fatigue, weakness, spasticity, bowel and bladder function, balance and my activities of daily living. Exercise burns calories and when incorporated with proper dietary habits helps control my weight.

But, incorporating exercise into my active lifestyle has been a challenge. It involves a process of careful planning and making small, progressive changes in my daily activities to accommodate the fatigue associated with the outcome. Using my knowledge of another piece of the "fatigue pie," I started exercising in the morning when my body temperature is the lowest, which is determined by the so-called "diurnal" temperature fluctuations of the body. Mammals tend to have a lower temperature in the morning around five or six o'clock, yet highest approximately 12 hours later at five or six o'clock at night. This concept may help explain why people with MS feel best in the morning and worst in the late afternoon.

Over time, I gradually built up a repertoire of exercises to cover different aspects of fitness – strength, endurance and flexibility – and gradually increased the intensity level of them all. At first it was hard, but fortunately, I was able to endure the hindrances of fatigue and weakness that tended to affect my activities of daily living, including work. But as I got stronger, I improved my endurance and lost weight. I was able to increase the exercise levels without significant interferences with my ability to function at home and work. For me to be physically fit, I needed to know how my body responded to exercise and nutrition, learn all the components of fatigue, know which exercises incorporating exercise into my daily routine.

Mental wellness

My mind, as well as my body, needs exercise to remain fit. For mental wellness I use my mind to share my MS experiences with others through teaching, lecturing and writing. I love to play bridge and do word games such as cryptoquotes that stimulate logic and skill. They all exercise my brain. However, I am aware of how physical fatigue affects my mental attention, which isn't caused just by overexertion. Heat-which isn't caused just by overexertion. Heat-related fatigue not only causes my body to fatigue but also causes mental "fuzziness." So, when my body is fatigued, for whatever reason, my ability to concentrate is diminished. There are no exercises to improve this phenomenon; I just have to be aware of the body-mind-fatigue relationship.

Recently, I shared my difficulty multi-tasking with my primary care physician. She suggested I explore a recently described condition called Adult Distraction Disorder or ADD, which is not to be confused with the more commonly described Attention Deficit Disorder found in children. The literature available for this ADD is not as comprehensive as MS, and is speculative but what I did find helped explain how individuals, such as myself, seem to repeatedly switch concentration from one project to another. It also seems to explain my tendency to procrastinate. I tend to put off finishing one project because I quickly change my attention to a different project. I have noticed my concentration is diverted more readily when I am mentally fatigued.

Being aware of my tendency to distraction was the first step in adapting to this phenomenon. I make a conscious effort to stay focused to the task at hand. Secondly, I let go of the attempt to multi-task by admitting to myself that I am not good at it. The third step was to adopt an attitude of not having to prove to anyone, including myself, that I am capable of competently completing tasks. I had been so motivated to dispel the myth of MS-related mental incompetence; I tried to do as many tasks as possible to show everyone I could do them. Ironically, this caused me to be come less competent! Now, instead of doing less because of trying to do too much, I do more by doing less. It's similar to speeding to get to the gas station before the gas tank gets to empty. The faster I go, the fewer miles per gallon I get.

Spiritual wellness

Admittedly, the weakest aspect of my wellness program is spirituality. However, I have come to terms with God and I know he is not responsible for me having MS. He's not punishing me for something I've done wrong. I'm not angry with Him for not taking the MS away from me, even though I believe He has the power to do so. On the contrary, I thank Him for giving me the strength to deal with these trials and tribulations in my life. However, beyond this concept my spiritual wellness needs to grow. Beyond my belief in God, I am not sure what spirituality really entails; it doesn't seem to be a priority at this time in my life and therefore I haven't put a lot of effort into finding how it could balance my scales of wellness.

Receive through giving

An often overlooked aspect of wellness is reaching out and giving back to society that which is received, otherwise known as altruism or philanthropy. I have a saying hanging on the wall in my den that states, "You give but little when you give of your possessions. It is when you give of yourself that you truly give!" I have definitely received back immeasurable rewards for all that I have given, but I'm not just talking about the plaques hanging on my wall. All of my volunteering resulted in my becoming more knowledgeable about MS and I was rewarded for my participation with awards and plaques. However, the ultimate reward is what I have learned about myself and my ability to cope with the adversities of disease and disability.

The ultimate quest

The greatest challenge in my pursuit to be well is the illness itself; it affects my lifestyle in many different ways. I have different physical symptoms as a direct result of the disease, each affecting my ability to move, think and respond to the disease, at various intensities and at various times. My MS is unique unto itself, taking on a personality of its own. MS is an entity affecting my body over which I have no control. How I respond to my disease is what I do have control over. Wellness helps me to meld my inner self together with the disease to become a single united body. Practicing wellness helps me to respond positively to the different physical, mental and emotional responses I have in living with the disease.

Some say, "I won't become my MS," but MS is a part of me. How could I not prevent that from happening? MS has some influence on every move I make and every goal I reach for. I go to sleep with MS and I wake up with MS. MS doesn't go away just because I want it to; it's a part of me. But, it is my attitude towards the illness that has helped me to sculpt who I became as a person living with MS. I had to answer the question, "Do I become my disease; or do I use the lessons of living with MS, synthesize what I have learned, adapt accordingly and become who I will be?" For the latter to be true, living within the Wellness Model is a must!

With all of those things in mind, this is where I stand with my MS. Although my loved ones, my teams of healthcare providers and the MS Society have helped me with the process, only I can determine what to do to maintain a healthy lifestyle. By living with the principles of wellness, not only will I be able to manage the waves of future adversities, I will also be better prepared when the cure and reversal of multiple sclerosis comes to fruition.

It will be no easy task to meet the challenge of strengthening the muscles and developing the coordination to reverse the MS symptoms that have plagued my body. I will need all the strength, endurance and mental discipline I can muster to have the energy to fight through hours, days and weeks of rehabilitation, but by being fit now, I will be prepared to endure the rigors of such a reversal. It will be a glorious time when the disease will no longer damage my body and I will be ready for that moment!

Courage isn't lack of fear.

Courage is acting in spite of it!